BUBBLES

Exploring mindfulness with kids

WRITTEN BY
HEATHER KRANTZ, MD

Mind Bubbles
Published by Herow Press
Bend, Oregon
herowpress.com

ISBN 978-0-9987037-1-8

First printing March 2017

A Note to Parents and Teachers:

Mindfulness is an innate human capacity that can easily be embraced by children. It involves paying attention to the present moment with an attitude of curiosity and acceptance. Simply said, mindfulness is being aware of what you are doing while you are doing it. Mindfulness cultivates emotional balance and the ability to pay attention. Children naturally live in the present. They *learn* to worry about the past and fret about the future. While worry may be necessary at times, it can easily overwhelm our thoughts and emotional life. By learning to direct our attention to our breath, mindfulness teaches us that thoughts and feelings are constantly changing. We don't have to judge them or identify with them. We have a choice. Learning mindfulness skills early in childhood can have immense benefit for future health, happiness, and well being. There is no better gift we can give our children.

Mind Bubbles presents a clear and simple approach to mindfulness by imagining thoughts and feelings as bubbles. Using soap bubble solution and a bubble wand is a fun way to demonstrate these concepts for children.

Dedicated to my husband and treasured partner in everything, Rob
my son and shining star, Rowan
my longtime friend and fellow children's book writer, Carrie
my comrade in mindfulness, Ray

I think lots of thoughts.
Do you?

I have lots of feelings.
Do you?

Those are mind bubbles.
Everybody has them.
They show what we think and feel.

Some are great!

Some can be really difficult.

Sometimes your mind can be so full of them it seems like more can't possibly fit! This can be confusing.

So what can we do about this?

Well, mind
bubbles are a lot
like soap bubbles.
Have you ever
blown bubbles?

Lots of bubbles
are floating around!

What happens to bubbles?

They float around
until they POP!

Every bubble pops.

And then new ones form.

We can think of mind bubbles as being just like soap bubbles. Every mind bubble pops. . . . . and new ones form.

But there are so many. . . .
And they just keep forming.
It can seem like too many.

What you really need to know is. . . . .
Everyone has mind bubbles!
Lots of them.
This is normal.

Mind bubbles may float around for awhile, but the interesting thing is that they always pop.

Thoughts and feelings change and new ones come along.

That's how our minds work.

Bubbles come.
Bubbles go.

There is a simple way to work with all the bubbles in your mind.

It's a gift you already own. . . .

Your BREATH!

Most of the time we ignore our breath.
But your breath is your friend.

So how can your breath help?

All of those mind bubbles will come and go no matter what. Sometimes it seems like you're watching a bubble movie in your head!

Instead of watching mind bubbles,
try noticing your breath.

Try it now.
Close your eyes and breathe
in and out.

Your breath is always with you.
It is friendly.

If you get distracted by more mind bubbles, just gently go back to noticing your breath.

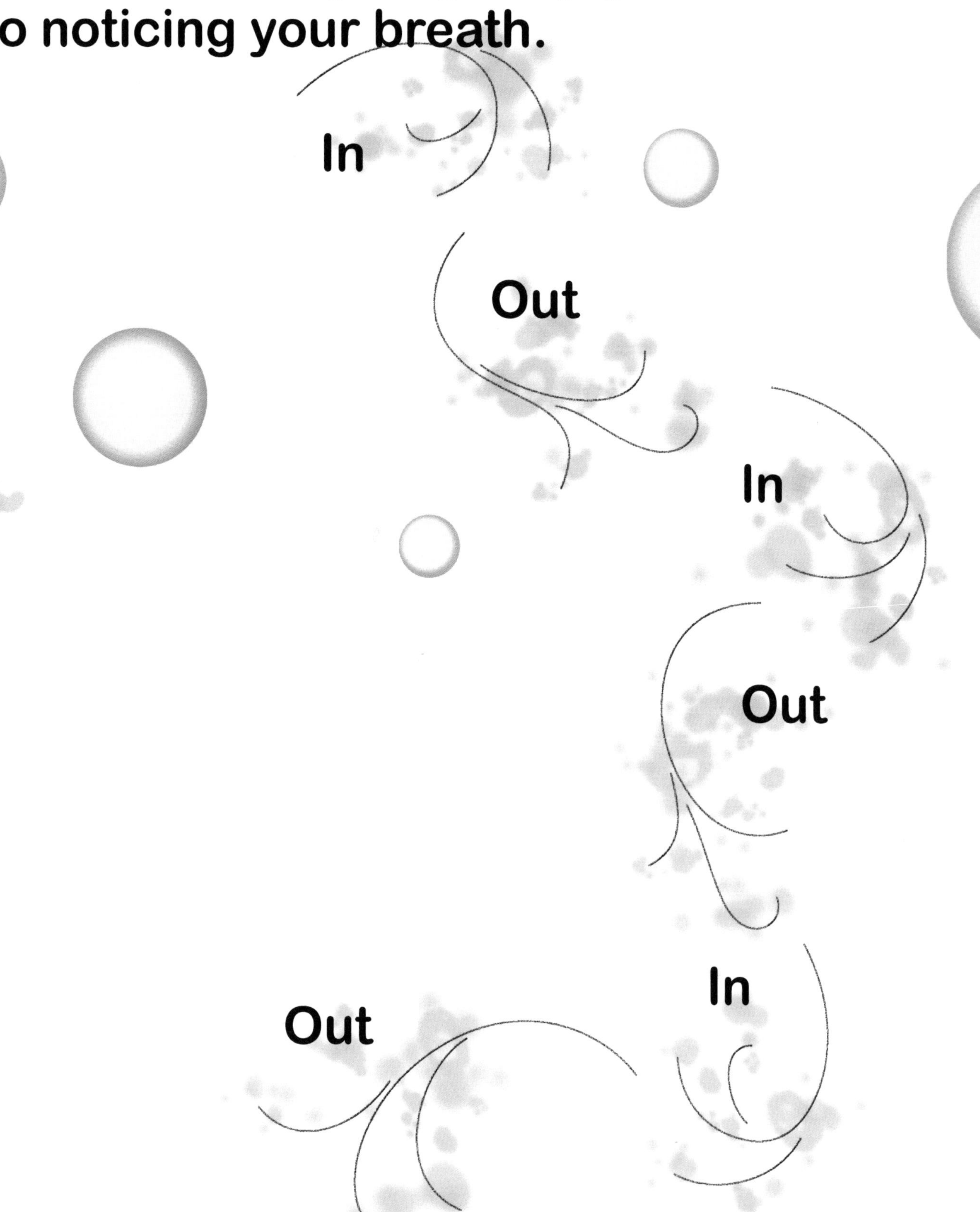

This takes practice.
Mind bubbles can be very distracting!

If you spend time noticing your breath moving in and out of your body. . . .

Pretty soon you will realize that mind bubbles still show up, but you can just allow them to be there.

You don't have to do anything about the bubbles.

If you go back to noticing your breath, each bubble will eventually pop!

And soon you will
feel calm and still.

And maybe
even happier.

And your breath becomes your BEST friend.

If you can be present right now with your breath and just be aware of all the mind bubbles. . . .

this is called Mindfulness.

So how do we remember this?

It's a SNAP!

Stop and breathe.
Notice mind bubbles.
Allow the bubbles to be there.
Practice again.

3-Minute Mindful Breathing Practice

(For Adult to Read to Kids)

Take a moment to sit comfortably with your back straight but relaxed. Let your eyes close gently and bring your attention to your breath—the in-breath and the out-breath. Let your attention simply be here now with your breathing.

(Pause for about 3 breaths.)

Thoughts might come. Let them go and stay with the breath. In and out.
Feelings might come. Let them go and stay with the breath. In and out.
There is no right way, no wrong way.
Just breathing.

(Pause for about 3 breaths.)

Staying with the breath. Noticing it. When your mind wanders, just gently bringing it back to the breath.

(Pause for about 3 breaths.)

Relaxing your body. Feeling the breath move through your body. Noticing the breath in the belly and in the nose and everywhere in between.

(Pause for about 3 breaths.)

Your body is calm and still. You are simply being here
in this moment with the breath.

(Pause for 2 breaths.)

As you hear the sound of the bell, gently open your eyes.
Allow yourself to stretch and bring your attention back to the room.

(Bell. You may choose to use another ending sound such as a chime.)

Heather Krantz, M.D. is an integrative medicine physician and mindfulness teacher. She worked for many years as an obstetrician/gynecologist and saw firsthand the disconnect between traditional medicine and true health and wellness. After completing a fellowship in integrative medicine, she now teaches Mindfulness-Based Stress Reduction, Mindful Self-Compassion, and mindfulness workshops and also practices mind-body medicine in Bend, Oregon.

Find her at HeatherKrantzMD.com and InSightMindfulnessCenter.com.

Lisa May is a medical illustrator based in Sisters, Oregon. She has a Masters of Science in Medical Illustration from the Medical College of Georgia. She has worked for nearly three decades illustrating and designing books and she has a passion for children's books and reading with kids. Find her at LisaMayStudio.com.

23852062R00026

Printed in Poland
by Amazon Fulfillment
Poland Sp. z o.o., Wrocław

IPHONE SE GUIDE FOR S

THE UPDATED, SIMPLE AND COMPLETE I

NON-TECH-SAVVY TO LEARN HOW TO USE YOUR NEW

IPHONE SE IN NO TIME

John Halbert

Table of contents

Introduction

The iPhone SE 2022 smartphone is designed, manufactured, and distributed as part of the iPhone product line by Apple Inc..

Along with 5G network support, the iPhone SE 2022 will have the same A15 Bionic processor as the iPhone 13. As a result, it will take the best pictures of any smartphone in its category and will have the best overall performance. Apple also claims that the new iPhone SE has a two-hour longer battery life than the iPhone SE 2020. This claim was made in the most recent earnings report by the company. In addition, a Touch ID-enabled Home button has been included to aid in the quick unlocking of the phone.

The iPhone SE 2022 is expected to be a huge success among both existing iPhone users and those who have not yet purchased an iPhone, due to its iconic design, increased performance, and more affordable price. This success is expected to come from both current iPhone users and those who have yet to buy an iPhone.

This book breaks down the functions of the iPhone SE 2022 in a straightforward manner, making it easier for seniors to understand and use them. This cutting-edge piece of gadget, as well as the numerous functions and tasks that can be accomplished with it, are thoroughly dissected throughout this instruction manual.

Let's get started.

Chapter 1: A Brief History Of The iPhone Since 2007

In the smartphone industry, 2007 was a watershed year. It changed the way we would think about, interact with, and feel about smartphones in general. 2007 was Apple's year.

This was the year that the late, great Steve Jobs would choose as his favorite of all the years he devoted to Apple products. The phones available in the pre-iPhone era were popular and thought to be smart before the original iPhone changed everything.

Mobile phones with miniature qwerty keyboards, mobile cameras, so-called internet access that barely worked, and some middling touch screen capabilities that functioned far worse than they do today were all available in 2007.

The worked on the outdated EDGE connectivity network, so even checking e-mails on mobile phones was a difficult task.

Checking voicemails would necessitate dialing a number specified by your network carrier, after which you would have to browse and listen through all the previous, irritating voices before finding the one you were looking for.

What about music players and other forms of entertainment on your phone? These features were only for show, and you should forget about using your phone in place of one of those dedicated music players from the late aughts, such as the iPod. At the time, no phone could reliably serve as your mobile media player. But, after all of these less-than-desirable smartphones, came the game changer that forever altered the mobile industry.

The smartphone, on which we have all come to rely, was introduced. The one we essentially can't live without, which began with a small, 3.5" screen and clunky features that we may now laugh at, was actually an amazing piece of technology that set the standard for all that came after it.

In a nutshell, the iPhone was years ahead of its time. Though this device did not sell well owing primarily to its high price, which was out of reach for most average consumers, it paved the way for a new world of mobile competition and experience, with incomparable operating systems and hardware.

People could choose their voicemails from interactive interfaces on this new device and select and play only those they wanted to hear. Because of support for faster network bands and highly optimized iOS, e-mail systems were now very simple and quick.

This small device had many amazing features that customers had never heard of before.

The multitouch support is a critical feature that we still use extensively today. Touch screens were relatively uncommon prior to the release of the first iPhone, and users could use multiple fingers on the display to perform a variety of extremely useful gestures.

In addition, iPhone introduced its Photos app, which displayed photos taken by its users in a way that no other mobile manufacturer had ever done with such ease. Similarly, the iPhone's video app was revolutionary.

The seamless app drawer was also far too good to pass up. It displayed all necessary apps and contained few useless apps, ultimately making iOS the most preferred mobile iOS we use to this day.

However, the Apple company that we know today can be divided into two major phases that behave and play with completely different strategies.

These phases correspond to the Steve Jobs era and the Tim Cook era, respectively. Both men served as CEO of the company and had a significant impact on it. Furthermore, after Apple fired then-iOS chief Scott Forstall in 2012, all Apple software underwent a major design shift.

The iPhone was created through the collaboration of three products: the iPod, a mobile phone, and a powerful internet communicating device. Clearly, these three components worked well together. The iOS operating system outperformed the Symbian OS, which deteriorated rapidly as the 2010s began.

Yes, iOS in 2007 was not what it is today; it had several flaws, such as the inability to change wallpapers from the default. There was no app store, and manually adding apps to the phone was nearly impossible.

There was no option for users to receive or share files or multimedia.

However, as time passed, we would soon see an incredible mobile OS in the form of iOS 11, which was first introduced in 2017. This new operating system emphasizes innovation, such as a focus on AR rather than VR, as well as the recently announced METAL 2 graphics processing.

Models:

- iPhone (2007–2008)
- iPhone 3G (2008–2010)
- iPhone 3GS (2009–2012)
- iPhone 4 (2010–2013)
- iPhone 4S (2011–2014)
- iPhone 5 (2012–2013)
- iPhone 5C (2013–2015)
- iPhone 5S (2013–2016)
- iPhone 6 (2014–2016)
- iPhone 6 Plus (2014–2016)
- iPhone 6S (2015–2018)
- iPhone 6S Plus (2015–2018)
- iPhone SE (1st) (2016–2018)
- iPhone 7 (2016–2019)
- iPhone 7 Plus (2016–2019)
- iPhone 8 (2017–2020)
- iPhone 8 Plus (2017–2020)
- iPhone X (2017–2018)
- iPhone XR (2018–2021)
- iPhone XS (2018–2019)
- iPhone XS Max (2018–2019)
- iPhone 11 Pro (2019–2020)
- iPhone 11 Pro Max (2019–2020)

- iPhone 12 Pro (2020–2021)
- iPhone 12 Pro Max (2020–2021)
- iPhone 12 Mini (2020–present)
- iPhone 13 (2021–present)
- iPhone 13 Mini (2021–present)
- iPhone 13 Pro (2021–present)
- iPhone 13 Pro Max (2021–present)

Chapter 2: iPhone SE Specs

The iPhone SE 3 was released on the eighteenth of March at a starting price of $249. The iPhone SE 3 presents users with the option of choosing three storages. The 64GB version is the basic version, and it comes at the price of $249. Depending on your size preferences, $479 will get you the 64 GB version, while for $579, you'll get the 256 GB version.

Specifications

The iPhone SE 2022 has a 4.77-inch LCD display.

It is powered by an A15 Bionic processor.

When it comes to storage, you have three options. They are as follows: 64GB, 128GB, and 256GB.

It is built with an aluminum frame and glass front and back.

Nano or Esim sim cards are available.

It is water-resistant for up to thirty minutes and dust-resistant to IP67 standards.

The iPhone SE 2022 is protected by an oleophobic coating on an Ion-strengthened glass.

There is no card reader.

The device ships with iOS 15.4, which can be upgraded to 15.4.1.

The CPU has six cores, and the GPU has four cores.

It has stereo speakers and a loudspeaker.

It is equipped with A-GPS, GLONASS, BDS, GALILEO, and QZSS.

The USB 2.0 version provides lightning-fast charging.

The fingerprint reader is located on the front of the device. Other sensors included are a proximity sensor, compass, accelerometer, barometer, and gyroscope.

The battery is non-removable and has a capacity of 2,180Mah.

The phone charges quickly. It takes about an hour to get from 0% to 100%. It can also be charged wirelessly with a Qi charger.

Apple iPhone SE3 vs SE2

	Apple iPhone SE 3	Apple iPhone SE 2
CPU	• Apple A15 Bionic	• Apple A13 Bionic
Body	• 138.4 x 67.3 x 7.3mm • 144g	• 138.4 x 67.3 x 7.3mm • 148g
Display	• 4.7-inch Retina HD LCD display • 1334 x 750p • True Tone technology • Haptic Touch support • 625 nits max brightness	• 4.7-inch Retina HD LCD display • 1334 x 750p • True Tone technology • Haptic Touch support • 625 nits max brightness
Cameras	• Primary: 12MP, f/1.8 • Front-facing: 7MP, f/2.2	• Primary: 12MP, f/1.8 • Front-facing: 7MP, f/2.2
Memory	• 4GB RAM • 64GB/128GB/256GB Storage	• 3GB RAM • 64GB/128GB/256GB Storage
Battery	• 2,018mAh • 20W wired fast charging • 7.5W Qi wireless charging	• 1,821mAh • 18W wired fast charging • 7.5W Qi wireless charging
Connectivity	• Sub6/mmWave 5G • 4G LTE • Wi-Fi • Bluetooth 5.0	• 4G LTE • Wi-Fi • Bluetooth 5.0
Water Resistance	IP67	IP67
Security	Touch ID	Touch ID
OS	iOS 15	iOS 15
Colors	• Red • Midnight • Starlight	• Red • Black • White
Material	• Glass back • Aluminum frame	• Glass back • Aluminum frame
Price	Starts at $429	Starts at $399

Chapter 3: Basic Terminology About Main Functions

Control Center: Control Center is a feature of the iOS operating system that allows iOS devices to quickly access critical device settings by swiping up from the bottom of the screen. It's your one-stop shop for instant access to dozens of iPhone controls, including media playback, brightness, volume controls, mobile connectivity, screen mirroring, and so on. This quick-access menu allows you to quickly access some of your iPhone's most frequently used and/or useful features and settings without having to launch the individual applications.

Airplane Mode: The iPhone and most mobile devices have an airplane mode. When this feature is enabled, all wireless signals from your smartphone are blocked. When enabled, an airplane icon will appear in the status bar at the top of your iPhone. Airplane mode disables cellular, Wi-Fi, and Bluetooth connectivity.

Cellular Data: To connect you to the internet, cellular data uses the same network infrastructure that is used for cellphone calls, which is made available by cellphone towers. Unlike Wi-Fi, cellular data is always available as long as you're within your mobile service provider's coverage area.

Wi-Fi: This is the control for turning on your iPhone's Wi-Fi connectivity. A Wi-Fi network is essentially an internet connection that is distributed to various electronic devices such as computers, tablets, smartphones, and so on by a wireless router. It allows these devices to communicate with the internet via a wireless router.

Bluetooth: This is a technology that allows data to be transmitted over short distances between devices. Bluetooth waves can only travel short distances and have a rapid frequency change.

Media Playback: This control allows you to manage media files that are currently playing. From this panel, you can pause or play a running media file, or skip to the next song.

Portrait Orientation Lock: This feature prevents your iPhone's display from switching from portrait to landscape mode when it is tilted beyond a certain angle.

Do Not Disturb: This feature mutes your iPhone, allowing you to ignore calls and other notifications while you attend a meeting, eat, sleep, or work quietly. When in silent mode, your iPhone receives and stores all calls, messages, and notifications.

Brightness Slider: The Brightness Slider allows you to control the brightness of your iPhone's screen manually. When you force-touch the brightness slider, you can also turn on or off True Tone, which automatically adjusts the brightness of your display based on the ambient lighting conditions in your immediate surroundings. Just beside the True Tone control switch is a Night Shift control, which allows you to manage the amount of blue light emitted by your iPhone's display.

Volume Slider: The volume control, or slider, on the control panel allows you to adjust your device's volume without having to press the volume rocker on the left side of the iPhone display. When you receive notifications, your device makes no noise and its display does not light up, but you can still view them by physically turning on the display.

Screen Mirroring: Screen Mirroring is a wireless method of simultaneously reproducing what appears on one device's screen on another device's screen.

The **flashlight** feature on your iPhone can be accessed via the control center. Your iPhone's camera flash also functions as a flashlight, which is a useful tool for improving vision in low-light situations. It is powered by the flash mechanism built into the primary camera unit on the back of your iPhone, and it is located near the camera's lens.

Timer: The clock application's Timer can be used to count down from a specific time to zero. After you've set the timer, you can put the iPhone to sleep by using other apps or pressing the Sleep button. The timer will continue to count down in the background and will emit a sound when the countdown is complete.

Calculator: The calculator app on your iPhone is a simple four-function calculating software that allows you to add, subtract, multiply, and divide. It also serves as a scientific calculator, capable of performing trigonometric and logarithmic calculations.

Camera: Tapping on the camera icon launches the camera app.

Depending on your preferences, additional controls can be added to the control center.

Chapter 4: How To Setup iPhone SE For The First Time

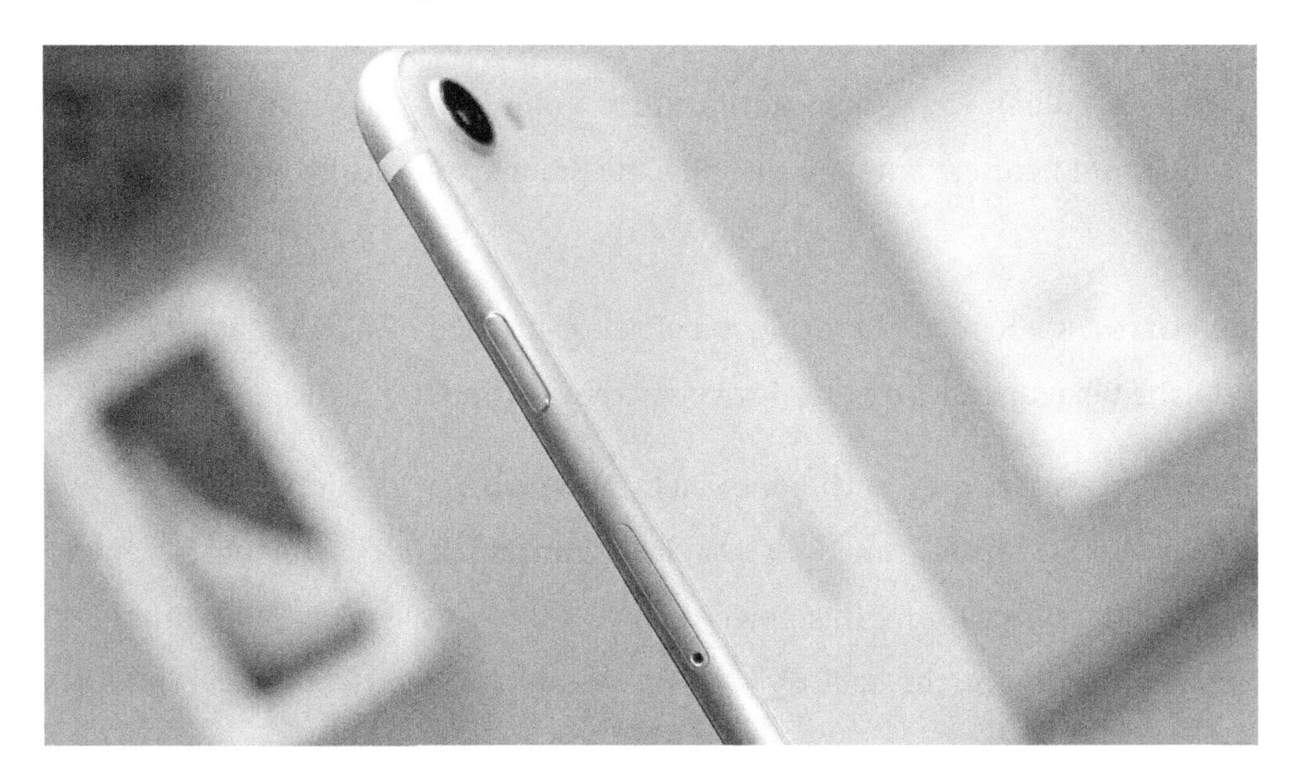

The first question you may have after purchasing a new iPhone SE is how to activate it, so you've turned to this guide for help. Here, I'll walk you through the process of activating and configuring your iPhone SE 2022 step-by-step.

- Turn on your iPhone SE by holding down the device's power button until the Apple logo appears.

- Next, you'll see "Hello" displayed in several languages. Go through the steps to start.

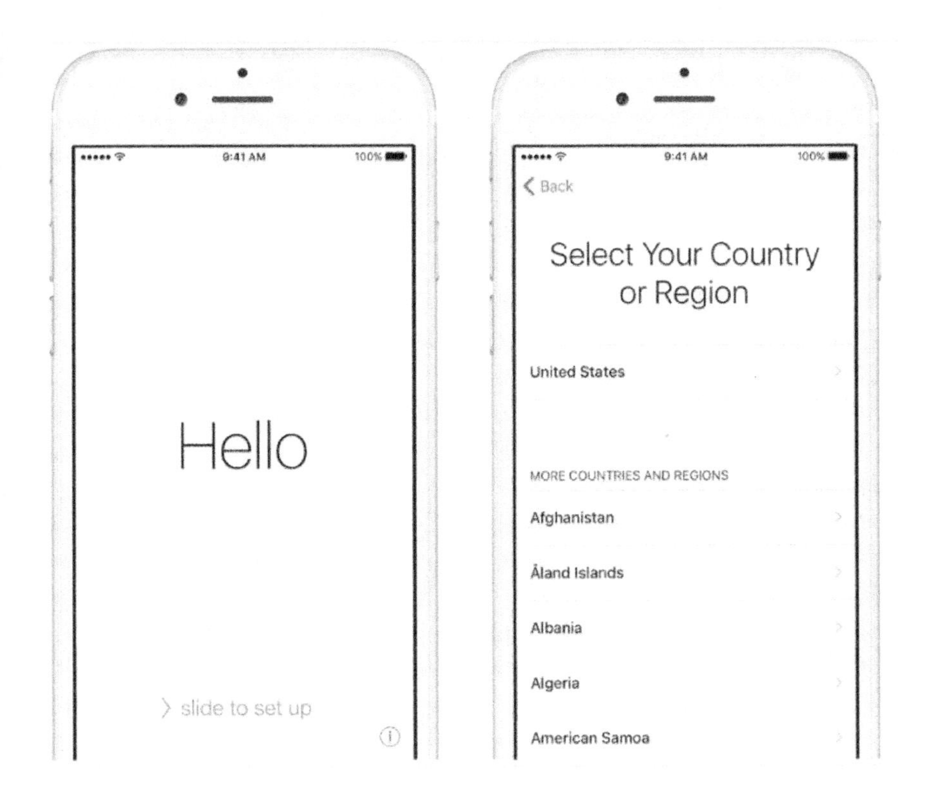

- Tap the home button and then select your language, and then pick your location (country or region). This option will change how the details appear on your smartphone, as well as contacts, date, time, etc.

- If you own an older iPhone running iOS 11 or newer, you can use the **QuickStart** option to automatically set up your new iPhone SE 2022. However, if you don't own an iPhone running iOS 11 or newer, just click on **Set Up Manually** to proceed.

- Make your choice by tapping the Wi-Fi network or selecting another alternative. If you don't have access to Wi-Fi, you can select **Use Cellular Connection** instead.

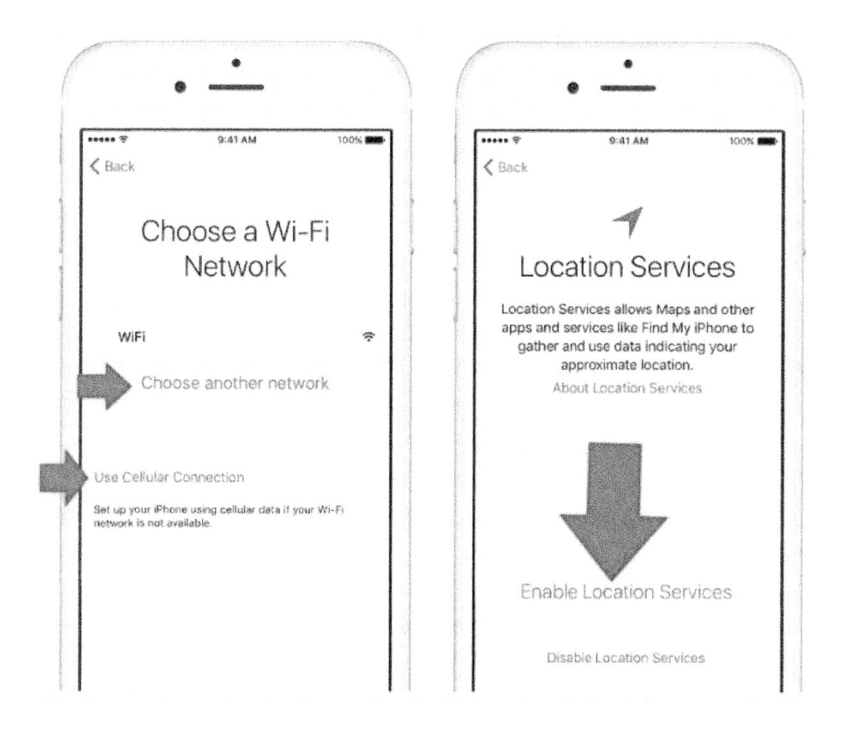

- On the **Location Service** page, select **Enable Location Services** to get personalized feeds based on your location or click **Disable Location Services** to decline.

- Proceed by setting up your Touch ID. This feature allows you to use your fingerprint to unlock your iPhone as well as make purchases. Select **Continue** and then follow the guidelines to configure it or click on **Set Up Later in Settings** to configure the option whenever you choose to.

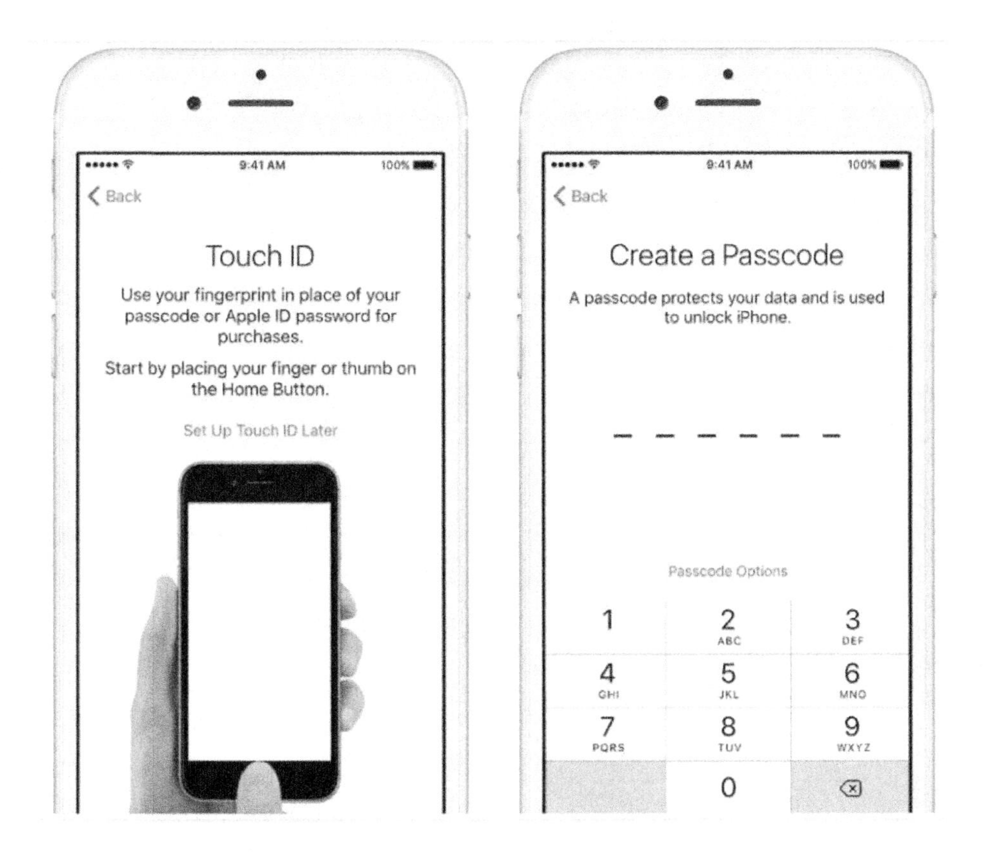

- Continue by setting up a six-digit passcode to add a security layer to your data. The passcode will be required when using Touch ID or Apple Pay. However, if you opt for a four-digit passcode, customized passcode, or don't need a passcode, click on **Passcode Options**.

- While on the **App & Data** window make a selection by choosing to restore from iCloud or iTunes backup, transfer straight from iPhone. Alternatively, select **Move Data from Android**. However, you can decline any of the options by tapping **Don't Transfer Apps & Data**.

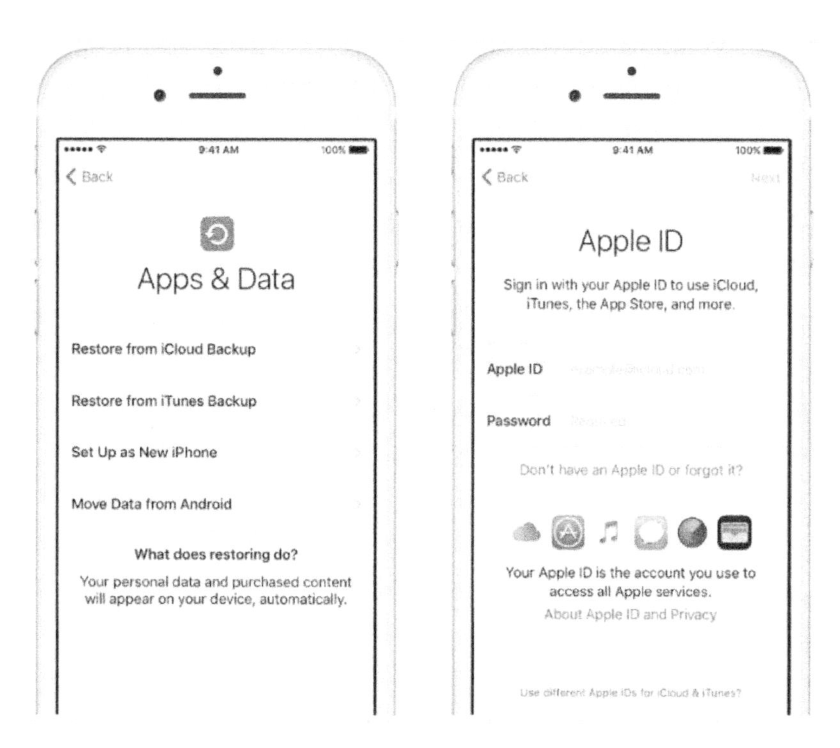

- Proceed by inputting your Apple ID and password, or choose **Forgot password**. Alternatively, tap "**don't have an Apple ID?**" to create an Apple ID. Also, you can skip the option and set it up later in the Settings app.

- Then, choose to share info with app developers and let the iPhone operating system (iOS) update automatically.

- Proceed by setting up Siri as well as other services or choose **Set Up Later in Settings**.

- On the next screen, choose to set up Screen Time as well as other display options or click **Set Up Later in Settings**. The Screen Time feature allows users to configure time limits for day-to-day app use.

- Then, click **Get Started** to start using your third-generation iPhone SE.

Backup iPhone to iCloud

You can only store a limited number of files for free by using iCloud to back up your iPhone. However, you may use iTunes on a computer or Finder on a Mac to make a backup of your iPhone SE. After you save a backup to your computer, you can move the data to an external hard drive. Using iCloud for backups is a breeze. You can choose to do it over Wi-Fi, or set up your iPhone to back up automatically, so you don't have to think about it.

- First, launch the Settings app on your iPhone SE.
- Then, click your name at the top of the Settings window.

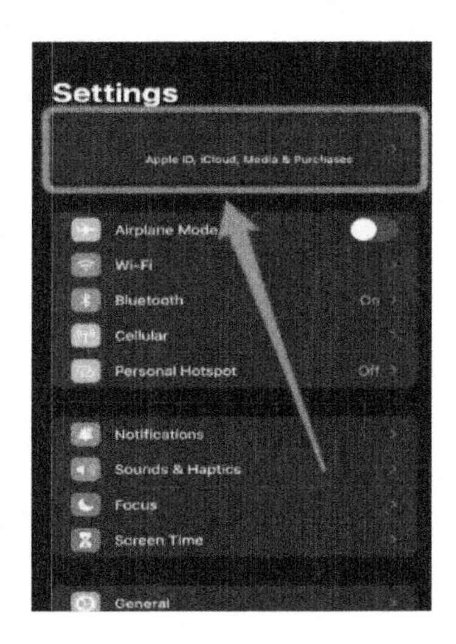

- While on the Apple ID screen, click **iCloud**.

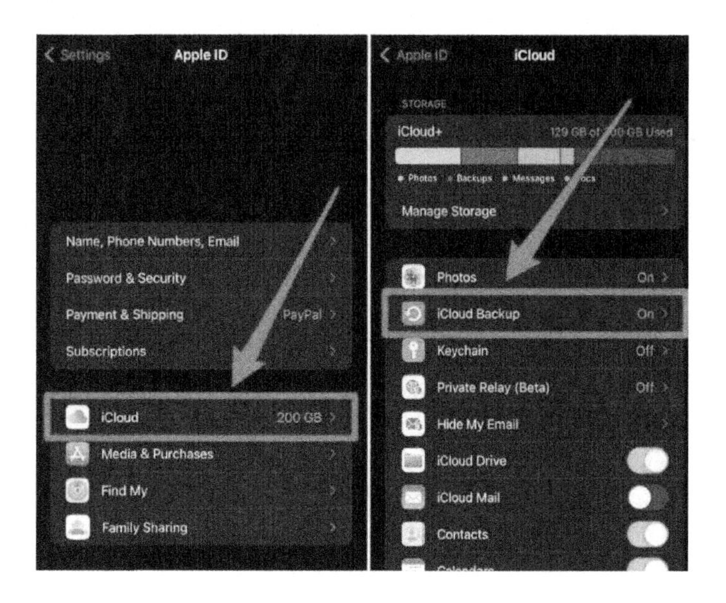

- Next, tap **iCloud Backup**.
- Ensure you toggled on all the data types you wish to back up.

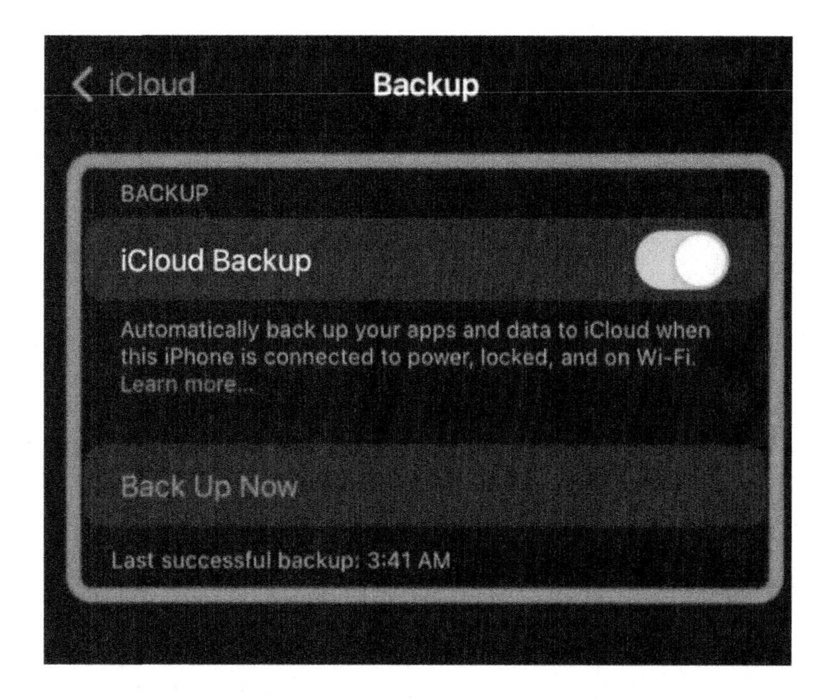

- Also, ensure you toggle on **iCloud Backup**. This will make your iPhone automatically backup whenever it's charging and paired to a Wi-Fi connection if you're not using it. As a result, it is recommended that you plug your phone in at night before you go to sleep so that your files can be backed up.

- Alternately, click on the **Back Up Now** option to manually create a backup instantly.

There are only 5GB of free storage when you create an Apple ID account. You'll quickly run out of storage space if you're using iCloud to back up numerous Apple devices, or even just one fairly loaded iPhone. You can choose from the three tiers of storage plans: 50 GB for $0.99 per month, 200 GB for $2.99, and 2 TB for $9.99 per month.

How to Use iCloud Private Relay

The iCloud Private Relay feature encrypts your internet traffic and routes it through two different internet relays. Your IP address, geolocation, and browsing history will be hidden from internet sites and network providers if you use this feature.

The service is only available to iCloud+ subscribers who pay between $0.99 and $9.99 per month. The iCloud Private Relay feature is limited to a single device. If you own a lot of Apple hardware, make sure you do these steps on each one.

- Launch the Settings app.
- Then, click on your name at the top of the Settings page.

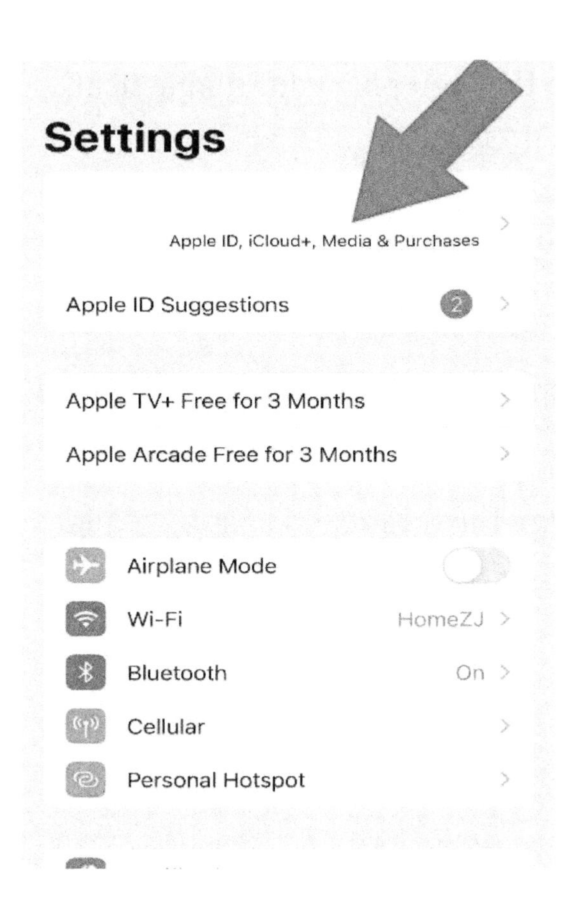

- Then, tap **iCloud**.

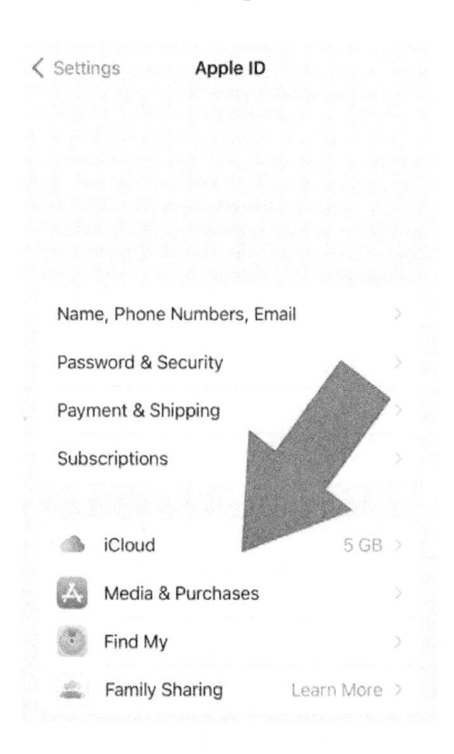

- From there, tap **Private Relay**.

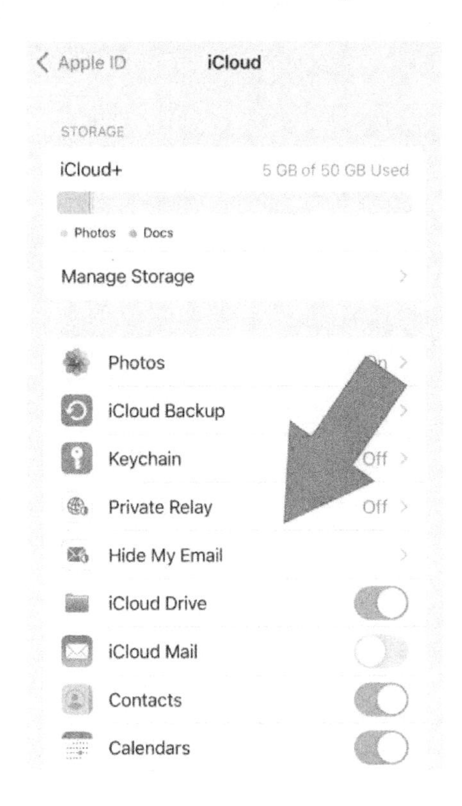

- Here, you'll see the explanation for Private Relay as well as a toggle button. Proceed by tapping on the toggle to make it green, it'll ensure the feature is enabled on your phone.

In addition, you can toggle on Private Relay for a particular Wi-Fi or cellular network by following the procedures below:

- Go to the Settings app homepage.
- Then, tap **Wi-Fi**. From here, you'll see your current Wi-Fi network as well as the list of available networks that are in proximity.
- Next, click the "**i**" beside your current network.

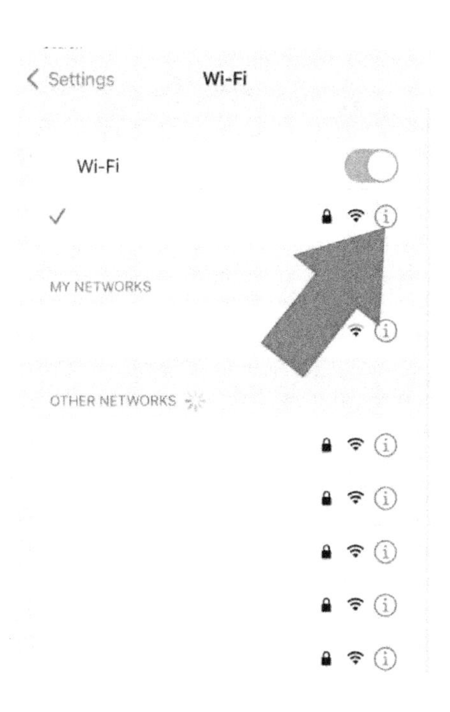

- From there, click on the toggle beside the **iCloud Private Relay** option.

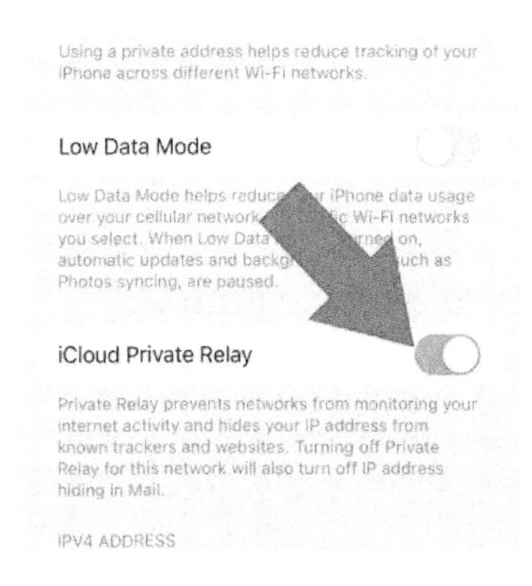

To turn on Private Relay for a particular cellular network, follow these steps:

- Go to the Settings app homepage.
- Tap **Cellular**.

- If there's only one line linked with your phone, click on **Cellular Data Options**.

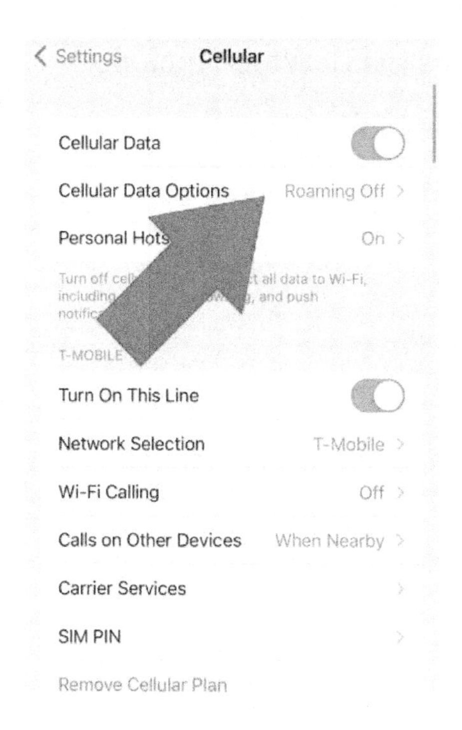

- And then turn on the toggle beside the **iCloud Private Relay** option.

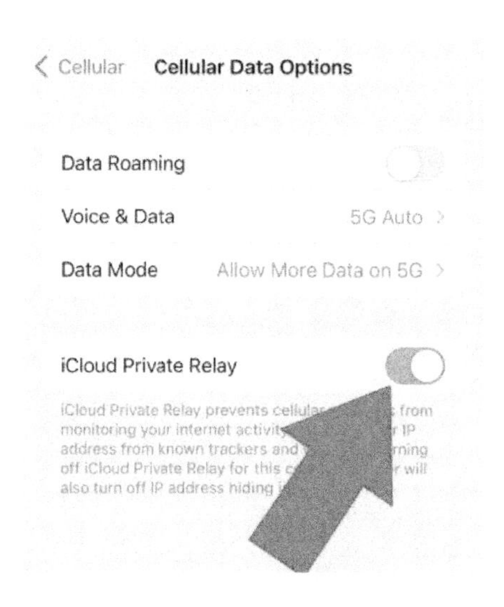

- However, if there are multiple lines, pick the line you prefer to activate Private Relay on, and then toggle it on.

Update iOS

Apple updates the iPhone operating system on a regular basis (iOS). Which includes new and improved features. You can update your iOS device by following the steps below:

Open the Settings app.

Click General from there.

Then, select Software Update.

You can now begin the download and installation of your update.

Chapter 5: Internet Setup

Use a Wi-Fi or cellular network to connect your iPhone to the internet.

Connect To Wi-Fi

1) Make sure that Wi-Fi is enabled by going to Settings > Wi-Fi and turning it on.

2) One of these options will be tapped:

- *A network:* Enter the password if necessary.

- *Other:* The other way around: It becomes a part of an unidentified network. Enter the network name, kind of security, and password for the secret network.

An iPhone is connected to a Wi-Fi network if the Wi-Fi symbol shows at the top of the screen. (Open Safari and look at a website to see whether this is true.) Reconnecting with your iPhone is automatic when you return to the same area.

Join Personal Hotspot

A Personal Hotspot may be shared by an iPad (Wi-Fi + Cellular) or an iPhone (Wi-Fi + Cellular).

Go to Settings > Wi-Fi, then select the name of the Personal Hotspot-sharing device.

Your Personal Hotspot password may be found under the Settings > Cellular > Personal Hotspot on the device you're using to share your Wi-Fi.

Connect Cellular Service

If no Wi-Fi network is available, your iPhone will connect to your carrier's cellular data network. If your iPhone isn't connecting, check the following:

1) Confirm the status of your SIM card.

2) Examine the Cellular configuration.

3) Check to see if your mobile data is turned on. On a dual-sim phone, go to Cellular Data, then check the line you've selected. The number of cellular data lines you can use is limited.

When an internet connection is required, the iPhone follows the steps below in order until one is established:

It makes an attempt to connect to the most recently used open Wi-Fi network available.

It identifies and connects to the Wi-Fi network you select from a list of available networks in the area. Or it connects to your service provider's cellular data network.

On an iPhone that supports 5G, you can use your cellular data instead of Wi-Fi. Under the name of the Wi-Fi network, you'll see a message that says, "Using 5G Cellular for

Internet." You can reconnect to Wi-Fi by tapping the Info button next to the network name and then selecting Use Wi-Fi for Internet.

If you don't have Wi-Fi, applications and services may send data over your carrier's cellular network, which may incur additional charges. Call your service provider for more information on your cellular data plan costs.

Chapter 6: ICloud Account, Apps Payment, How To Setup Credit Card Or Paypal

Apple ID

This is an Apple account that lets you download and install games and apps from the Apple store, purchase books, movies, and music from iTunes, sync your contacts, reminders, and calendars through iCloud as well as use iMessage and Facetime in the messages apps.

Create an Apple ID

- Open the Settings app.

- Navigate to the top of the screen and click on **Sign in to your iPhone**.

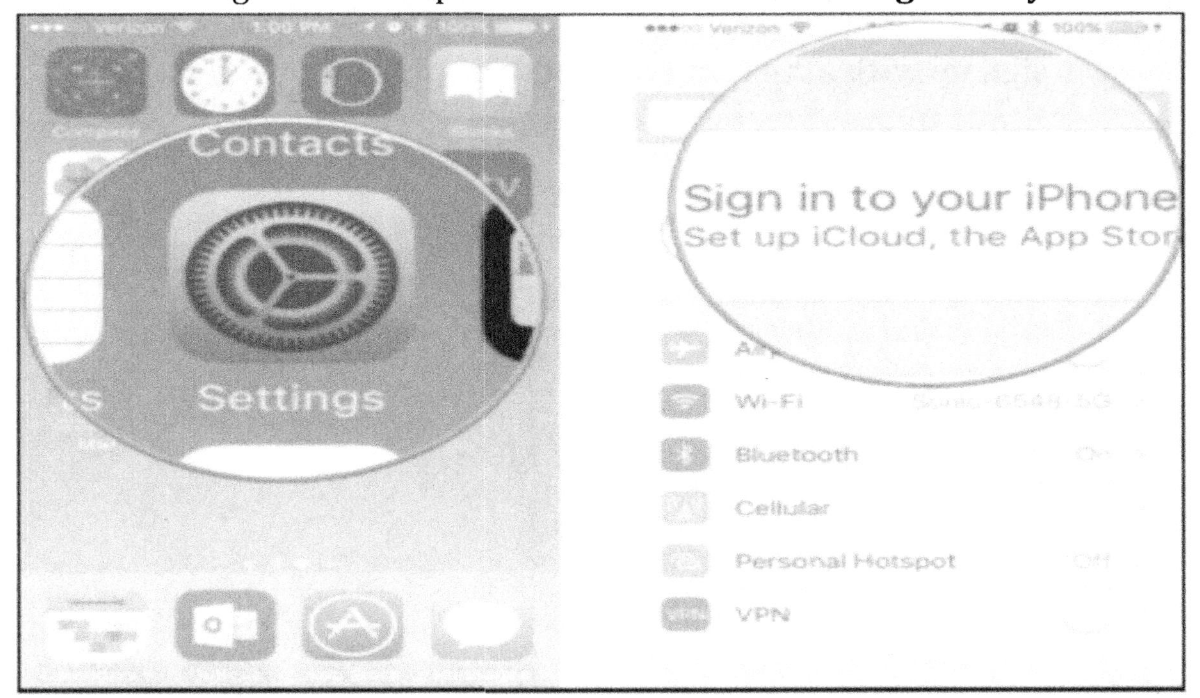

- Click on **Don't have an Apple ID or forgot it?**
- On the next screen, select **Create Apple ID**

- Input your date of birth, then tap **Next**.

- Input your names: first and last, then tap **Next**.
- Choose to **sign up with a current email address** or choose to **get a free iCloud email address**.

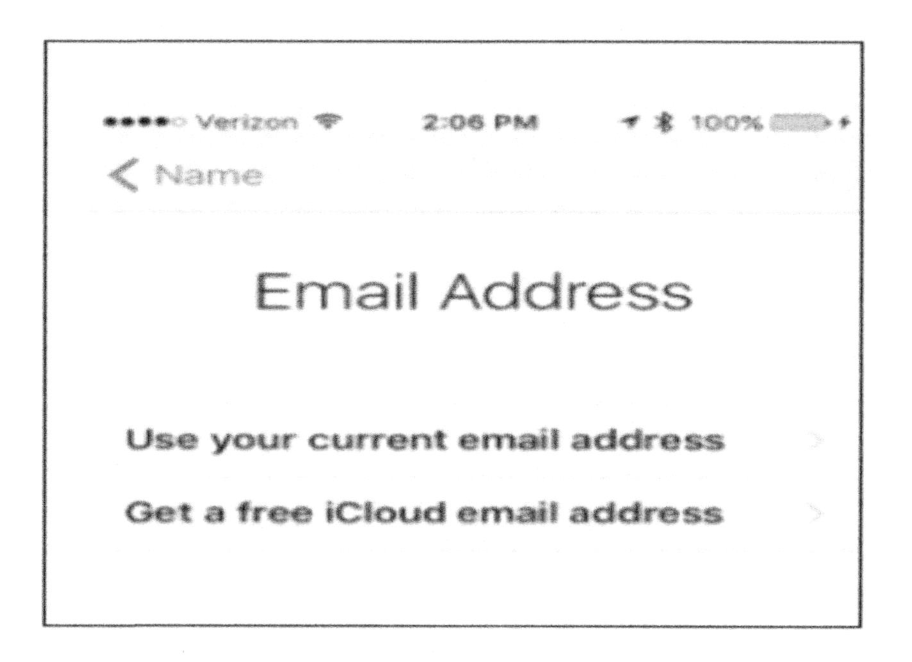

- Input your email address and create your desired password.
- Repeat the password.
- Set a security question and input the answer. You are to select three security questions and input their answers.
- Click on **Next.**

- Accept the Terms and Conditions.
- Choose to Merge or not to merge, to sync iCloud data from calendars,

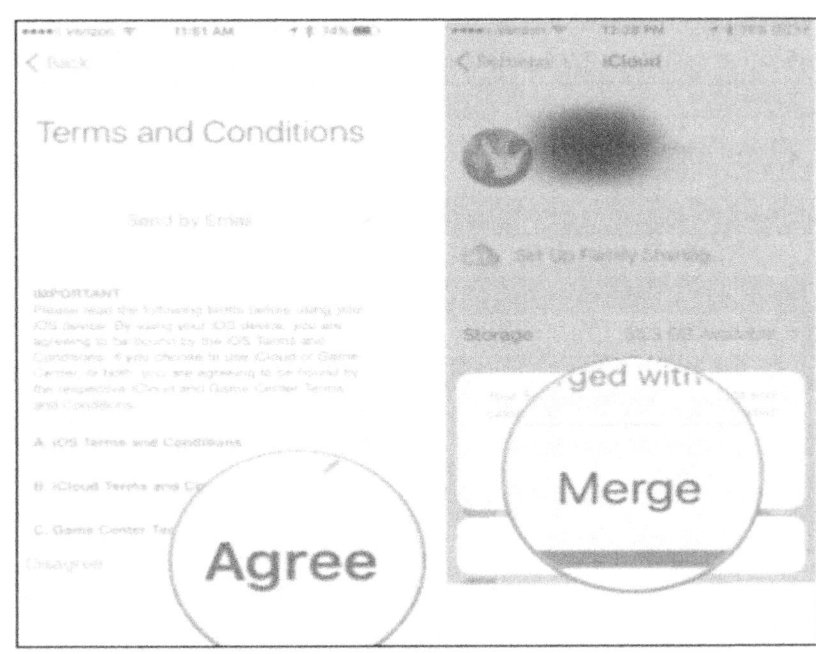

contacts, Safari, and reminders.

- Click on **Ok** to confirm that you want the Find My enabled.

Sign In to iCloud With an Existing Apple ID

- Open the **Settings** app.
- Navigate to the top of the screen and click on **Sign in to your iPhone.**
- Input your login details, then click on **Sign In.**

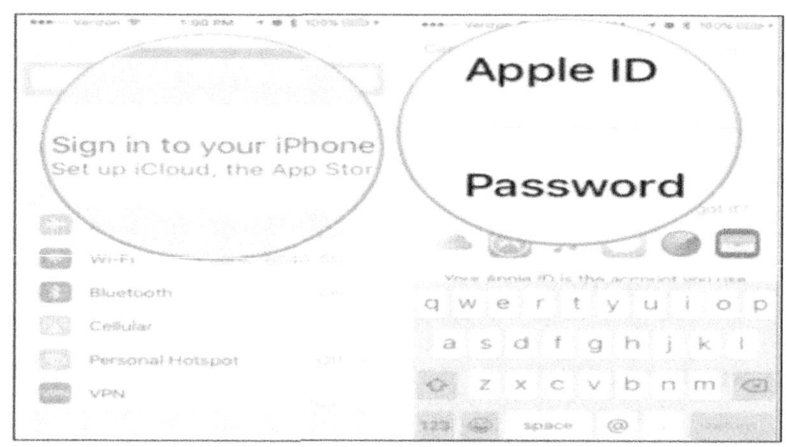

- Enter your passcode when prompted.
- Check that your iCloud photos are in the way you like them.

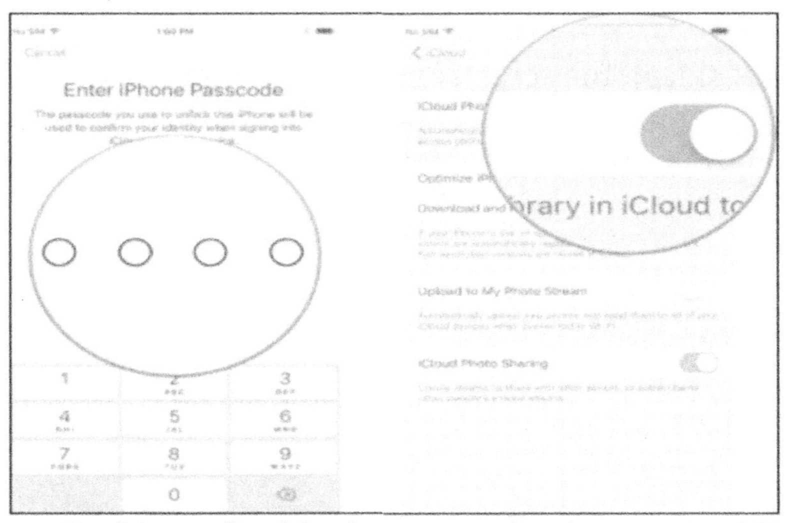

- Enable or disable the option for Apps using iCloud, depending on your preference.

Sign Out of iCloud

- Open the Settings app.
- Navigate to the top of the screen and click on your **Apple ID**.
- Go to the bottom of the screen, then click on **Sign Out.**

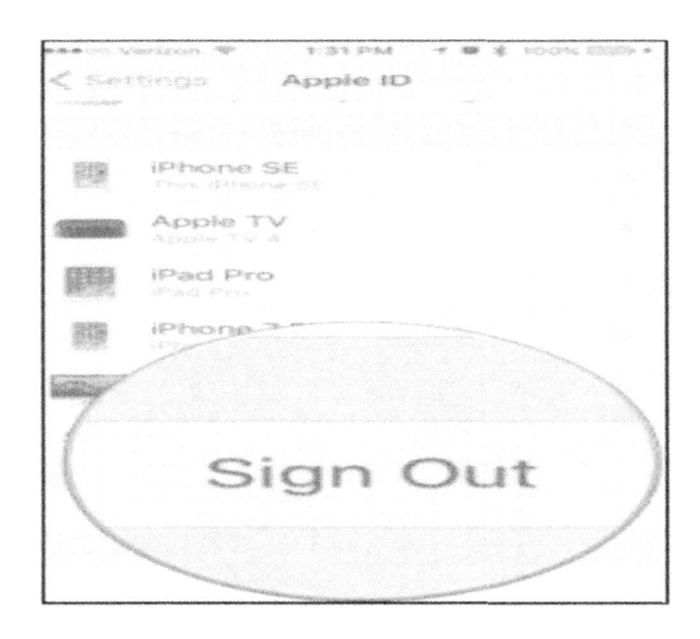

- Input your Apple ID password for this account, then click on **Turn Off.**

- Toggle the switch for all the data you want to keep on your device.
- Navigate to the top right side of the screen and click on **Sign Out.**
- Click on **Sign Out** again to confirm your action.

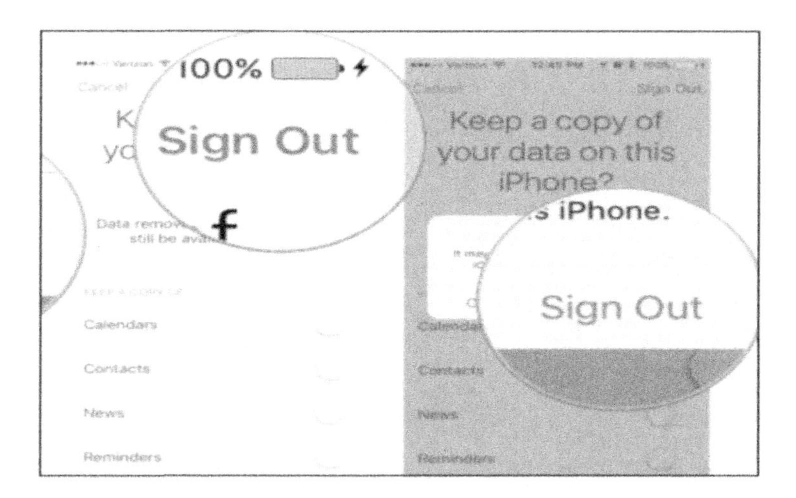

Apple Pay

Apple Pay allows you to make online and in-store purchases on your iPhone, just by tapping the home button and scanning your fingerprint. This is a fast and secure way to make purchases using your debit and credit cards.

Add a Card for Apple Pay

- Launch the wallet app on your phone, then tap the ⊕ button at the top side of

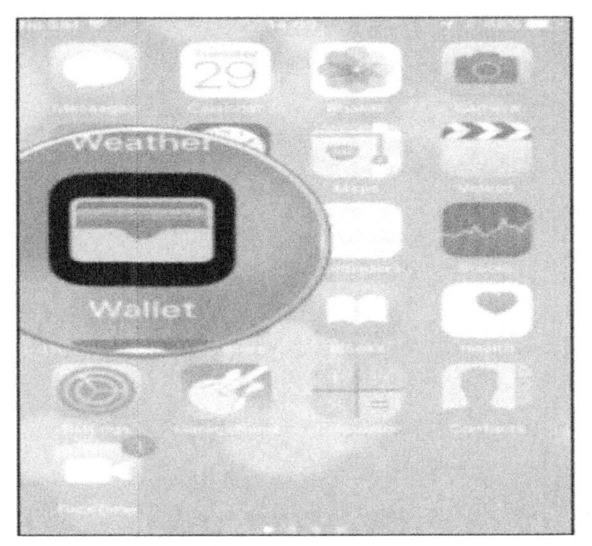

your screen.

- Tap **Next**.

- Scan your card information or click on **Enter Card Details Manually** to input it manually.

- Click on **Next** on the details screen.
- Manually type the expiry date and security code of the card.

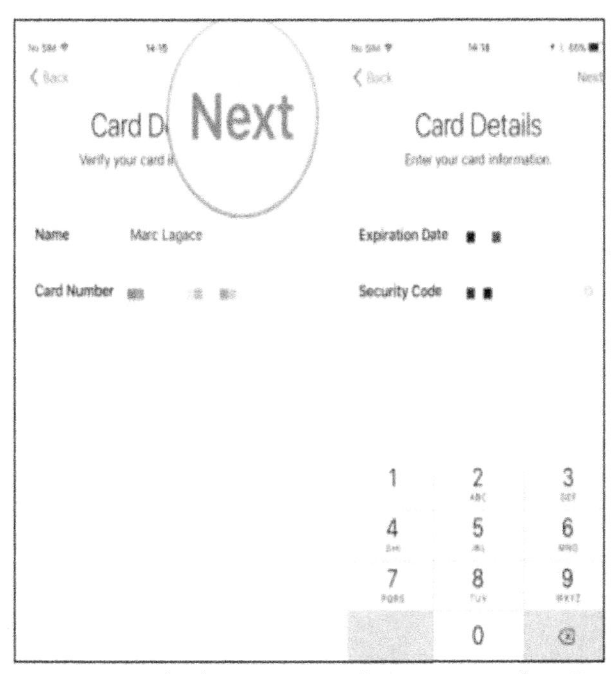

- Click **Next** and agree to the Terms and Conditions.
- Tap **Agree** again.

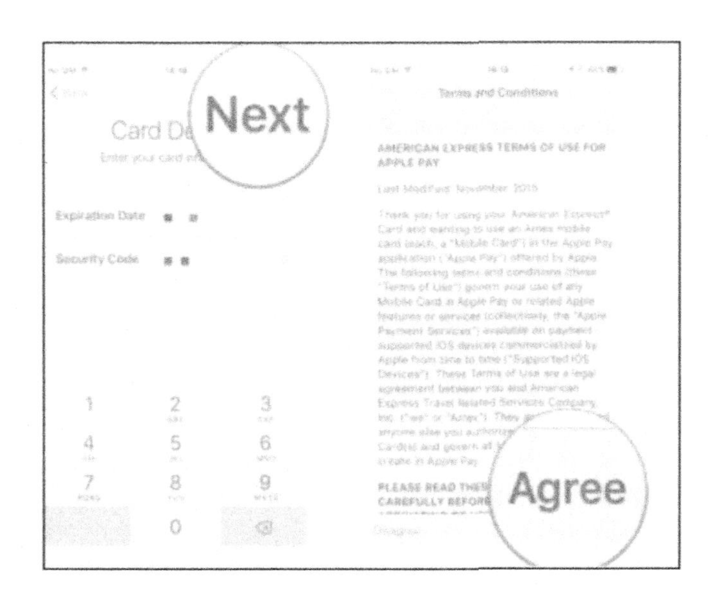

- Select your verification method and click on **Next**.

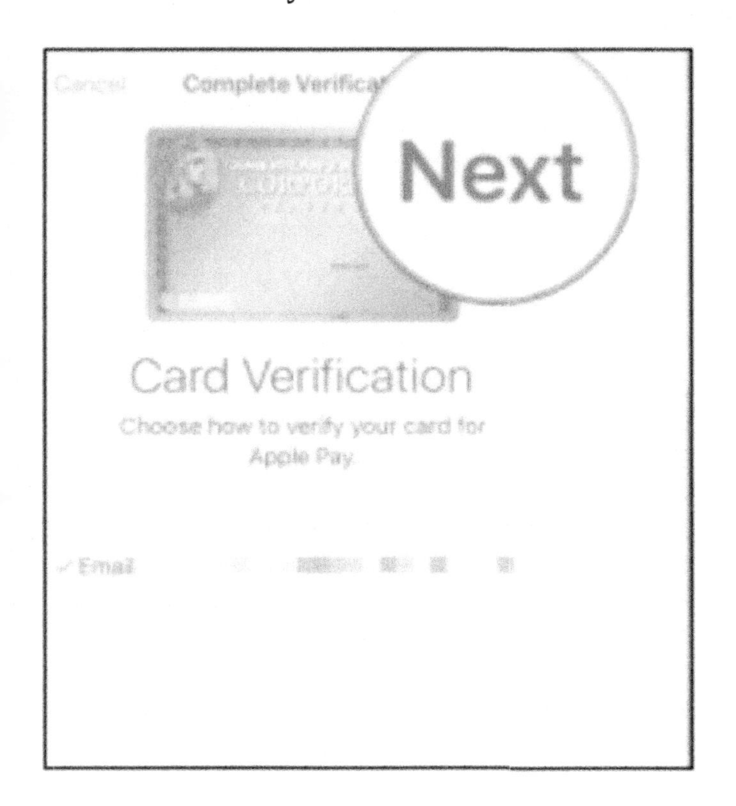

- Click on **Enter Code.**
- Input the verification code sent to you via text, call, or email.

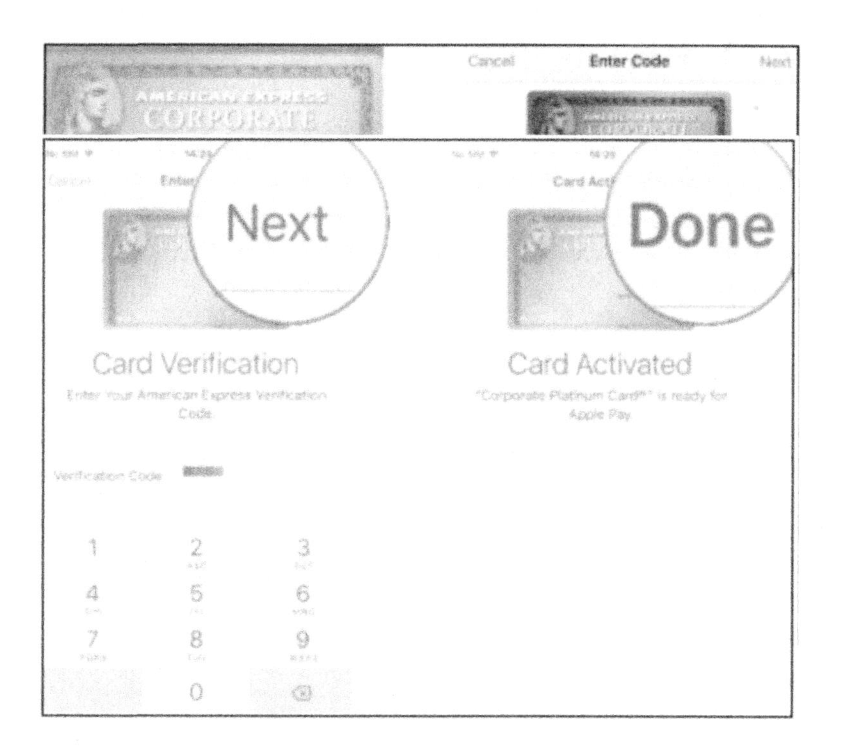

- Click on **Next**, then click on **Done**.

- Repeat the steps above to card more cards in the future.

Note: credit or debit cards with flat numbers will have to be inputted manually. Only cards with embossed numbers can be scanned into the Apple Pay wallet.

Change the Default Card for Apple Pay

While you can always switch between cards when performing transactions, using the default card makes your transaction fast and easy. Here is how to set a default card:

- Open the Settings app on your phone.
- Click on **Wallet & Apple Pay.**

- Then click on **Default Card.**

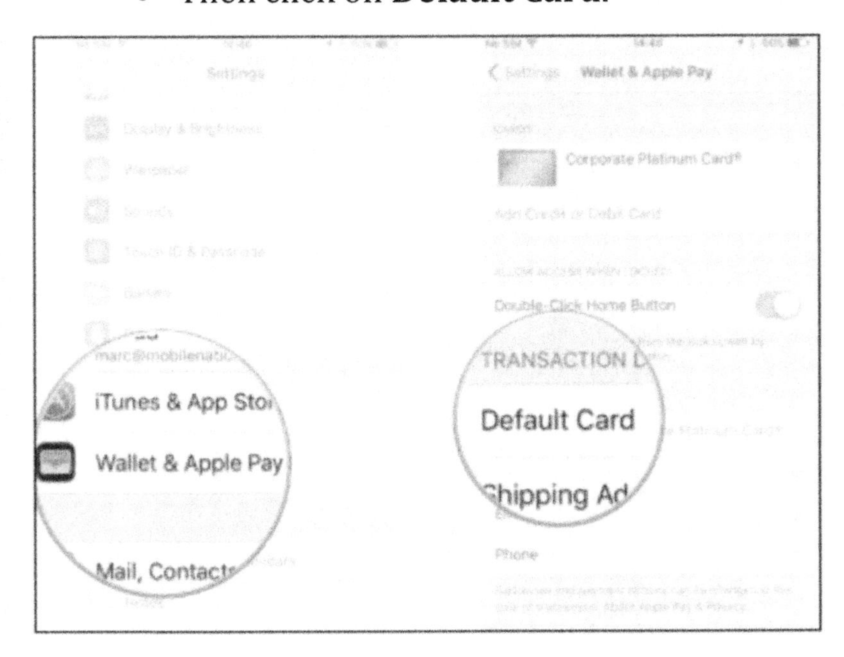

- Click on the card you want to set as your default.
- When next you want to make a purchase, your default card will be used for payment.

<u>Remove a Card from Apple Pay</u>

Here is how to remove a card when lost, stolen, or for other reasons:

- Open the Settings app on your phone.
- Click on **Wallet & Apple Pay.**
- Click on the card you wish to delete.
- Then scroll to the bottom and click on **Remove Card.**

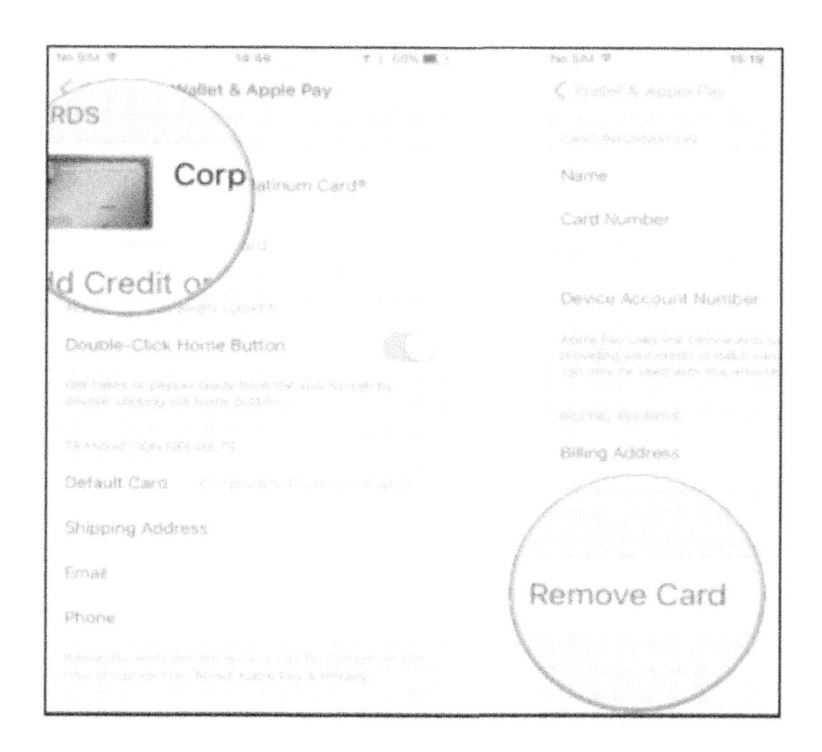

Note: this will only remove the card on your iPhone SE. You will have to manually remove the card on all other devices that have the card linked. An alternative is to remove the card remotely via iCloud. Below is how to do this.

Chapter 7: Must-Have Apps To Interact With Others And How To Set Them Up

Set Up Mail

Add your email accounts to your device so you can read and send emails.

1. Select the Mail application from your Home screen.

2. Choose an email service provider.

Please keep in mind that Google has been chosen for this presentation. If your email provider isn't on the list, click More. Follow the on-screen instructions to enter the necessary account configuration information. If you do not remember your e-mail settings, please use the Mail Usage preferences to contact your e-mail or service provider. Depending on your provider, you may be redirected to its external portal to register. Log in to your account by following the instructions.

3. Input your email address and tap **Next**. Input your password and tap Next.

Note: To manually modify email settings (such as server settings and security type), navigate to the Mail panel and pick the relevant account> account name> Advanced. If you are unable to locate this information, please contact your email provider. If remote security management is required for your company's server, you will be requested to set security features. To proceed, click OK.

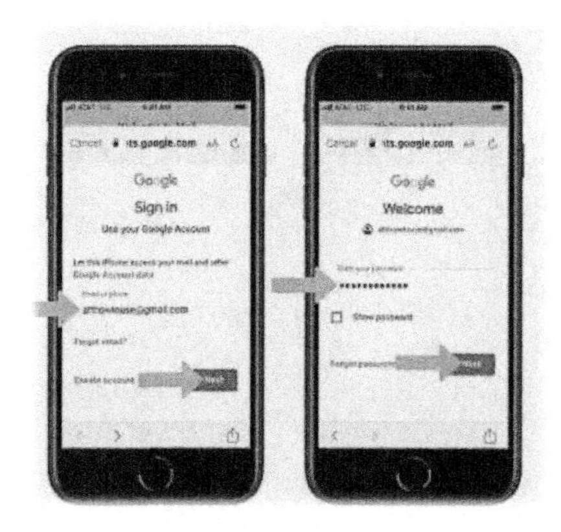

4. Set the desired account synchronization options and tap Save.

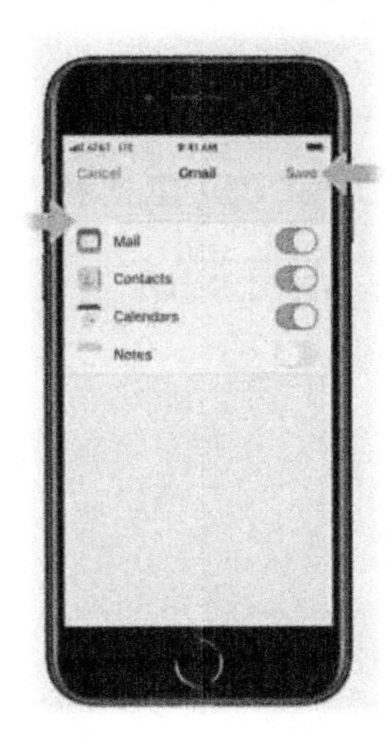

5. The Mail program is now set up with your email address. If this is the only account you've configured on your iPhone, you'll be sent to your Inbox. If you've created extra accounts, you'll be brought back to the main screen.

Note: If you've created multiple email accounts, choose the default from the Application settings>Email accounts menu. Scroll to and select Mail> Default account> Choose the desired account. If your company's server requires remote security management, you will be asked to configure security features. Continue by following the on-screen instructions to generate a password. More information can be found at Apple Support. Set up an email account on your iPhone. Check here if you're having trouble configuring your iPhone's mail.

Check Your Mail

You can read emails, add contacts, and preview email content without having to open them in the Mail app.

Examine the email

Click the email you want to read in the Inbox.

Email preview and options list

You can preview an email if you want to read its contents without fully opening it. Tap and hold an email in your Inbox to see its contents as well as a menu of options for replying, sending, and other actions.

Display a larger preview of each email

You can read an email's contents without opening it completely. Tap and hold an email in your Inbox to see its contents and a menu of options for replying, sending, and more.

Display the entire chat

Go to Settings>Mail and turn on Thread Organizer (under Threads).

Tip: You can also change additional settings under Settings> Mail, such as Collapse read messages or Show recent messages at the top.

Display the Za and Kp tags in your Inbox

Select Show / KP stickers from the Settings> Mail menu (below Message List).

You can also check your Za / Kp mailbox, which saves all communications sent to you. To reveal or hide it, go to the top left corner and click the Back button, then Edit, then "To or Share."

Make someone a VIP or add him to your contacts

Tap the person's name or email address in the email, and then do one of the following:

Add these people to your contacts: click Make a new contact or add to an existing one.

You can enter phone numbers, email addresses, and other information.

Add the following to your VIP list: Select Add to VIP.

Send Mail

In the Mail app, write and edit emails from any of your email accounts, use a custom email signature, add tags to addresses outside of specific domains, and more.

Write an email

Click the Assemble button.

Touch the email and then enter the message.

Tip: Use the on-screen keyboard to try swiping from one letter to another to type, raising your finger just for each word.

To change the formatting, click the Expand toolbar button on the formatting bar above the keyboard, and then click the Text Format button.

You can change the font style & color of the text, use bold or italics, add a bulleted or numbered list, and more.

Include recipients.

Enter the recipients' names in the To field.

As you type, it will suggest people from your contacts, along with their email addresses if they have more than one.

You can also open the contacts and add recipients from there by clicking the Add Contact button.

If you're sending a copy, go to the Share / Hidden notification field and choose one of the following options:

In the Kp box, enter the names of the people to whom you are sending a copy.

In the Cap box, enter the names of people you don't want other recipients to see.

When entering recipients' names, you can rearrange them in the address fields or drag them from one address field to another, such as the Bcc field if you don't want their names to be displayed.

Using the camera, capture an email address

You can use Live Text to scan an email address written on a business card, a billboard, or anything else using the Mail app on your iPhone. This allows you to send emails quickly without having to manually enter an address.

A photo of the business card with the provided email address and live text is displayed in the bottom half of the screen. A blue input button is present. In the top right corner of the screen, there is a draft email with the same email address as the recipient.

Then, in the To box, select Scan Email Address Scan.

Place the iPhone inside the camera frame so that the email address is visible.

Press the "enter" key when the yellow box with the recognized text appears.

To extract an email address from a picture, use the same Live Text method.

Send a copy to yourself automatically

Go to Settings> Mail and enable Always Bow Alone (in the Composition section).

Add more email accounts

Navigate to Settings> Mail> Accounts> Add Account, and then choose an option.

Switch the receiver from Kp to Bcc

After you've entered the recipients' names, you may rearrange them in the address fields or drag them from one address box to another, such as the Bcc field if you don't want to show their names.

Make your email signature unique

You may change the email signature that displays at the bottom of every email you send.

- Go to Settings> Mail, and then choose Signature (in the Edit section).
- After you've touched the text box, you may update your signature.
- In your email signatures, you can only use text.
- If you have several email accounts, click On account to establish a separate signature for each one.

Send email from a different account

If you have more than one email account, you may choose which one to send an email to.

- Click the Share / Hidden box, From, in the draft email.
- Select an account by tapping the From box.

Examine addresses that are not in certain domains

When you send an email to someone who does not belong to your organization's domain, the recipient's name may be highlighted in red to inform you.

- Navigate to Settings>Mail>Highlight Addresses (under Composition).
- Enter the portions of your body that you don't want to be highlighted in red.

Multiple parties may be imported, separated by commas (for example, "apple.com, example.org").

Reply To Mails

The Mail program allows you to respond to emails.

Respond to an email

- Touch email, click More Actions, and then tap Reply.
- Enter your answer.

Tip: Use the on-screen keyboard to try swiping from one letter to another to type, raising your finger just for each word.

When replying to an email, mention some text

When you reply to an email, you can include the sender's text to clarify what you reply to.

- In the sender's email, touch and then hold the first word of the text, then drag to the last word. (See Select, Cut, Copy, & Paste Text on iPhone.)
- Click the More Actions button, press Reply, and enter a message.
- To turn off the referral recess, go to Settings> Mail> Increase Reference Level (in the Syntax section), then turn off Referral Level Increase.

Message Setup

Within the Messaging software, you can send text messages to other iPhone, iPad, iPod touch, or Mac users via SMS / MMS or iMessage over Wi-Fi or mobile service. Texts sent and received via iMessage are not included in your mobile messaging software's SMS / MMS licensing, but may incur data charges on mobile networks.

Text messages delivered via instant messaging may include images, videos, and other data. You can observe what other people type and provide reading certificates to notify them when their messages have been read. iMessage messages are encrypted before transmission for security reasons.

Log in to iMessage.

To begin, navigate to Settings> Messaging.

Activate iMessage.

Sign in to iMessage with the same Apple ID you use to access your Mac and other Apple devices.

If you use the same Apple ID to sign in to iMessage on all of your devices, all of the messages you send and receive on your iPhone will appear on your other Apple devices. Send a message from any device within range, or use Handoff to start and finish a conversation on one device and continue it on another.

On your iPhone, iPad, or iPod touch, go to Settings> Messaging and enable iMessage.

Launch Messages on your Mac and perform one of the following actions:

Enter your Apple ID and password if this is your first time logging in, then click Sign In.

If you're already signed in and want to change your Apple ID, navigate to Messaging>Settings>iMessage.

SMS / MMS messages sent or received on your iPhone are displayed on all of your iOS devices and on your Mac.

Utilize iCloud Messaging

To enable or disable Messaging, navigate to Settings> [your name]> iCloud (if not already enabled).

iCloud saves a copy of every message you send and receive on your iPhone. Additionally, when you sign in with the same Apple ID on a new device that supports iCloud messaging, your entire chat history is displayed immediately.

Because iCloud stores your messages and attachments, you may discover that you have more available space on your iPhone when you need it. When you delete messages, entire conversations, or attachments from your iPhone, they are permanently deleted from all other Apple devices that support iCloud messaging.

Receive And Send Text Messages

Send and receive text, picture, video, and audio messages with the Messaging app. You may also add motion effects, Memoji stickers, iMessage applications, and other features to your messages.

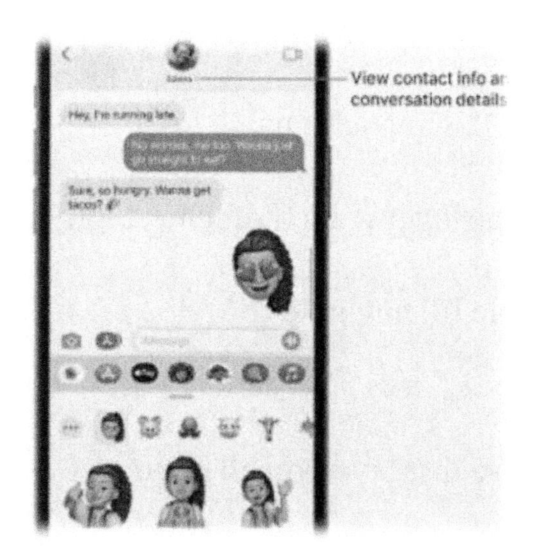

Send a message

You have the option of sending a text message to one or more recipients.

- At the top of the screen, hit the Compose button to start a new message or tap an existing message.
- Enter the recipient's phone number, contact name, or Apple ID in the appropriate fields. Alternatively, click the Add button and then pick contacts.
- To send an SMS MMS message from another line on dual SIM devices, press the visible line and then pick another line.
- Enter message in the text box, then hit the Send button to send it.
- A warning symbol appears if the message cannot be sent. To send the message again, press the alert.
- Drag the message bubble to the left to see when a communication was sent or received.
- Click the name or phone number at the top of the screen to examine the specifics of a discussion. You may change a business card, share your location, see attachments, opt out of a group conversation, and more by tapping a contact.
- To return from the conversation to the message list, hit the Back button or drag on the left border.

Respond to a message

Siri: "Send a message to Eliza and inform her tomorrow," you can say.

"Read Bob's last message" "Answer, this is fantastic news"

Alternatively, you might perform the following:

In the Messages list, touch the conversation to which you wish to respond.

To discover contacts and material in discussions, drag the Messages list down and enter your search terms in the search field. Alternatively, you may choose from the recommended contacts, websites, photographs, and more.

Enter your message in the text box.

To replace text with an emoji, hit the Next keyboard button, Emoji button, or Next keyboard button, and then touch each highlighted word.

To send your message, click the Send button.

You can swiftly react to a Tapback message (for example, thumb or heart). Tapback after double-clicking the message bubble to which you wish to respond. In a discussion, you may also respond to a particular message. See In a discussion, respond to a particular message.

Add your name and picture

When you start or respond to a new message in the Messages app, you may share your name and picture. Your image might be a Memoji or a bespoke one. When you first launch Messages, follow the prompts on your iPhone to pick your name and picture.

To alter the name, picture, or sharing choices, open Messaging, select More Options, Edit Name and Photo, and then choose one of the following:

Modify your profile photo by clicking Edit and selecting an option.

Modify your name: Tap the text fields where your name appears to change it.

To allow or deactivate sharing, click on the button next to Name and share photographs (green indicates it is enabled).

Modify who can view your profile: Select the Automatic sharing option (Name and photo sharing must be enabled).

You may also utilize the name and picture from Messages for your Apple ID and My Contacts card.

Pin the discussion

You may pin specific conversations to the top of the message list so that the individuals with whom you talk the most are always at the top.

Perform any of the following:

Swipe right after the discussion and press the Pin button.

Drag the chat to the top of the list by touching and holding it.

At the top of the message list, you may start some dialogues.

Perform any of the following:

Hold the discussion in your hand, then drag the message to the bottom of the list.

Touch and hold the chat for a few seconds, then hit the Unpin button.

Change from Messages to audio or video calling on FaceTime

You may initiate an audio or video call with the person you're conversing with in a Messaging session using FaceTime.

Press in the Messaging Conversation.

Select either FaceTime audio or FaceTime video.

How To Install Facebook And Other Social Apps On Your iPhone

To use Facebook on your device, you need to have it installed. To install Facebook, you need to set up your device for internet ad have your Apple ID.

To install Facebook:

- Tap on the App Store app on the home screen of your device.
- On the app store page, tap on the search icon at the bottom right side of your device.
- Type Facebook on the search bar and click on the first option.
- On Facebook page, tap on GET and follow the instructions on the screen of your device to get it installed.
- Tap on the home button to return to the home screen.

Follow the above steps to install every other relevant Apps you want.

Chapter 8: How To Setup Camera And How To Get The Best Photos/Videos

This chapter will teach you how to take pictures with the Camera application on your iPhone. Select from camera modes like photo, video, portrait, & Pano mode.

Open The Camera Application

To enter the Camera application, simply swipe left on your Lock screen or touch the Camera application icon your Home Screen.

Note: For your protection, a green dot would appear in the upper right corner of your display when using the Camera.

Switch Between Camera Modes

When you open the Camera application you will always meet the app in Photo mode. You can use photo mode to snap Live & still pictures. Swipe to the right or left on your camera screen to pick any of the following modes:

- ➔ Video: Record a video.
- ➔ TimeLapse.
- ➔ Slo-mo: Record a slow-motion video.
- ➔ Pano
- ➔ Portrait: Use deep effects in your pictures.
- ➔ Square: Use square ratio to snap pictures.

Zoom In Or Zoom Out

To zoom in or out, launch the Camera app and pinch open or closed on the camera screen.

Take a photograph or video.

Press the Shutter button or any of the volume controls.

Turn On Or Off The Flash

When you need it, your iPhone flash activates automatically. To use the flashlight manually, simply press the Flashlight button to turn it on or off. Touch the Camera Controls button, then the Flashlight button under the frame to toggle between On, Auto, and Off.

Use A Filter To Take A Picture

Use filters to add color effects to your photos.

Launch the Camera app, select Photo or Portrait mode, and then tap the Camera Controls button, followed by the Filter button.

Swipe left or right to view the viewer's filters; click on one to use it.

Set a timer

Set a timer to give yourself enough time to prepare for the shot on your camera.

To start a timer, press the Camera Controls button, then the Timer button, then the Shutter button to begin the countdown.

Take a Live Photograph

A Live Photo captures what happens before and after the shot, including sound, so you can see and hear it later.

Launch the Camera program.

Make sure the camera is in Photo mode and that Live Photo is turned on.

When you enable Live Photo, the Live Photo icon appears at the top of the camera screen. To activate or deactivate Live Photo, press the Live button.

To take the Live Photo, press the Shutter button.

To play a Live Picture, click on the thumbnail image in the lower right corner of your screen, then hold down your mouse button to play the video.

Use Burst Mode to capture action shots.

Burst mode allows you to capture moving objects or take a series of quick photos so that you have a large number of images to choose from. Burst shots can be taken with both the front and back cameras.

Start the Camera program.

Swipe the Shutter button left.

The counter would indicate how many photos you had taken.

Stop by raising your fingers.

Click the Select button after selecting the images you want to save from the Burst thumbnail.

Click the circle in the bottom-right corner of each image you want to save as a separate image, then tap the Done button.

To delete the entire Burst, click the thumbnail and then tap the Trash button.

Pose for a Selfie

You can use your front-facing camera to take photos or record videos.

Launch the camera.

Press the Camera Selector button to switch to the front camera.

Place your iPhone in front of you.

To take a picture or start recording, press the Shutter button or any of the volume buttons.

Make A Video

Swipe to Video mode after opening the Camera app.

To record, press the Record button or any of the volume buttons. While recording, you can do any of the following:

To take a picture, press the white Shutter button.

Pinch your screen to zoom in and out.

To stop the recording, press any of the volume buttons or the Record button.

Record A Quicktake Video

A Quick-Take video is a video recorded in Photos mode. While recording a Quick-Take video, you can lock the Record button and continue to take still pictures.

1. Open the Camera in Photos mode, then long-press the Shutter button to record the QuickTake video.

2. Drag the Shutter button to the right and raise your finger to enter hands-free recording.

- You would see the Shutter button & the Record button under the frame, touch the Shutter button to snap pictures while recording.

- Swipe up or pinch open to zoom in.

3. Press the Record button to stop recording.

Record A Slow-Motion Video

When a video is recorded in Slo-mo, the slow-motion effects are not visible until the video is played back. You can edit the video so that the slow-motion feature begins and ends at a specific point.

Swipe to Slo-mo mode after opening the camera.

To start and stop recording, press any of the volume buttons or the Record button.

If you want to play a portion of the video in slow motion while the rest plays normally, click the video thumbnail and then the Edit button. To select the segment to be played in slow motion, draw a vertical line beneath the frame viewer.

View Your Pictures

1. Open the Camera application, then click the thumbnail image in the bottom-left part of your display.

2. Swipe to the right or left to view your recent pictures.

3. Touch the screen to display or conceal the controls.

4. Touch All Photos to check out all your videos & pictures in the Photos application.

Use Live Text With Your iPhone Camera

You can use Live Text to copy and share text, open webpages, send emails, and make phone calls from the text in the camera frame.

Open the Camera app, then position your phone so that the text is visible in the camera frame.

Click the Live Text button when you see a yellow frame near the visible text.

Use the grab points to highlight text, then do one of the following:

The text should be copied.

Choose All of the text in the frame.

Text can be shared using Mail, Messages, AirDrop, and other services.

Click on the site, number, or email address on your display to access it, call it, or send it through an email.

To return to the camera, press the Live Text button.

Scan A QR Code With The Camera

You can utilize your iPhone camera to scan QR codes for links to applications, tickets, sites, coupons, etc. Your phone's camera will automatically detect & highlight a QR code.

1. Open the Camera application, then set your phone in a way that the code can be seen on the screen.

2. Touch the notification that pops-up on your display to access the appropriate site or application.

Chapter 9: Health And Fitness

How To Share Your Health Statistics Using The iPhone's Health App

You may share health data recorded in the Health app with relatives, and those who care for you, such as health warnings and trends.

Share Your Health Information With A Close Relative Or Friend

Individuals with whom you share health information may read health notifications such as high heart rate and irregular rhythm alerts. You can also share alerts for major developments, such as a sharp drop in activity.

You must first add someone to your contacts list before you can share with them, and they must have an iPhone running iOS 15 or later.

Tap Sharing at the bottom of the screen.

Take one of the following actions:

Enable sharing for the first time by tapping Share with Someone.

Distribute to an additional contact by clicking "Add another person" and then "Next."

Use the search form to find someone in your contacts list.

To select someone, tap on their contact information.

Select Manually Configure or See Suggested Topics.

Topics for discussion should be chosen.

Scroll down to see all subjects on one page, then click Next to proceed to the next screen.

Share is followed by Done.

Your invitation appears as a notification on your contact's iPhone as well as on their Health Sharing screen, where they can accept or decline it.

You will be notified if your invitation is accepted.

Communicate With Your Doctor About Your Health

You can share health information with your doctors (such as heart rate, exercise minutes, sleep hours, test results, and heart health alerts). Doctors can access the data through a dashboard in their electronic health record systems (only in the United States; on systems that support Health app data). Distribute to Provider).

Tap Sharing at the bottom of the screen.

Take one of the following actions:

Allow sharing for the first time: Choose "Share with your doctor."

Select "Share with another physician" to collaborate with a second provider.

To find your supplier, click Next, then one of the recommended providers, or use Search.

If it appears, tap Connect to Account, enter the user name and password for the patient web portal associated with that account, and then follow the prompts on the screen.

In addition to sharing your health data, connecting to your account allows you to download your account's health records to Health.

Select topics to discuss with your doctor

Scroll down to see all subjects on one page, then click Next to proceed to the next screen.

Share is followed by Done.

Examine or change the information you share with others

Tap Sharing at the bottom of the screen.

Tap the name of a person or a healthcare provider.

Scroll down and tap View Shared Data.

Make any necessary changes before clicking Done.

Stop sharing data with a contact or a supplier

Tap Sharing at the bottom of the screen.

Tap the name of a person or a healthcare provider.

Stop sharing or delete an account by selecting Stop Sharing or Delete Account.

How Health And Fitness Data May Be Shared Through Applications And Gadgets

You may provide permission to other applications to exchange health and fitness data with Health. For instance, if you install a workout application, the app's activity data may display in Health. Additionally, the exercise app may read and use data supplied by other devices and applications (such as your heart rate and weight). If you did not provide an app permission to share data with Health during the app's setup, you may grant it afterwards. Additionally, you may deactivate an app's permissions.

- At the upper right, tap your profile photo or initials.

If your profile image or initials are not visible, touch Summary or Browse at the screen's bottom and then scroll to the top.

- Select Apps or Devices from the drop-down menu under Privacy.

The screen displays a list of the objects for which access to Health data was requested.

- To modify an item's access, touch it and then toggle the authorization to write to—or read from—Health on or off.

Transmit data about your health and fitness in XML format

You may export all of your health and fitness data from Health in XML format, which is a widely used standard for data exchange across applications.

- At the upper right, click your profile photo or initials.

If your profile image or initials are not visible, touch Summary or Browse at the screen's bottom and then scroll to the top.

- Tap Export all health data and then decide how to share it.

How To Monitor Your Walking Stability With The iPhone's Health App

When you carry your iPhone in a pocket or holster around your waist, the Health app assesses your balance, strength, and gait using unique algorithms. You may get an alert if your steadiness drops or remains low, and the alert can be shared automatically with someone nearby. Additionally, Health may demonstrate techniques to assist you to improve your walking stability. (Apple iPhone 8 and newer.)

The Lock Screen with a notice for Low Walking Stability.

Receive Alerts When Your Steadfastness Is Low Or Very Low

Tap your profile photo or initials in the upper right corner.

If your profile image or initials are not visible, tap Summary or Browse at the bottom of the screen and scroll to the top.

By clicking on it, you can access the Health Checklist.

After clicking Set Up for Walking Steadiness Notifications, follow the steps on your screen.

To view your alerts, go to the lower right corner and select Mobility, then scroll down and select Walking Steadiness Notifications.

View Data Regarding Your Walking Stability:

Press Browse, then Mobility in the lower right corner.

Consistency in Walking (you may need to scroll down).

To learn more about the three steadiness levels, press the Show Information button (OK, Low, and Very Low).

Learn how to improve your walking stability by doing the following:

Click Browse, then Mobility in the lower right corner.

Scroll down and select Exercises to Help You Walk More Stably.

How Your Health Data Can Be Viewed On Your iPhone Through Health App

You can examine all of your health and fitness information in one location with the Health app. For instance, you may monitor your symptoms over time and your progress toward movement, sleep, and mindfulness objectives, among others.

Analyze your health statistics:

After collecting data for an extended period of time, Health may notify you of noteworthy changes in data categories such as resting heart rate, step count, and quantity of sleep. The trend lines indicate how much and for how long certain indicators have changed.

- At the bottom left, tap Summary, and then scroll from the top to Trends to observe any recent trends.
- If Health identifies patterns, you may take the following actions:

  To get further information about a trend, tap its graph.

  View other trends by tapping View Health Trends.

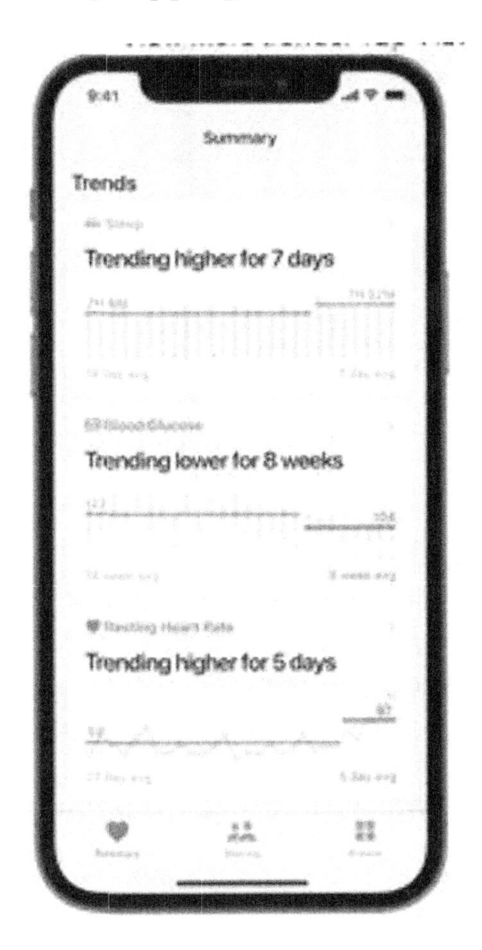

The Summary panel displays statistics on trends, including graphs for Sleep, Blood Glucose, and Resting Heart Rate.

To get alerts about your health trends, navigate to the Summary page, press View Health Trends, touch "Manage notifications," and then toggle on Trends.

View your personal highlights:

At the bottom left, tap Summary, then scroll down to get a summary of your recent health and fitness statistics.

To get further information on a highlight, hit the Details button.

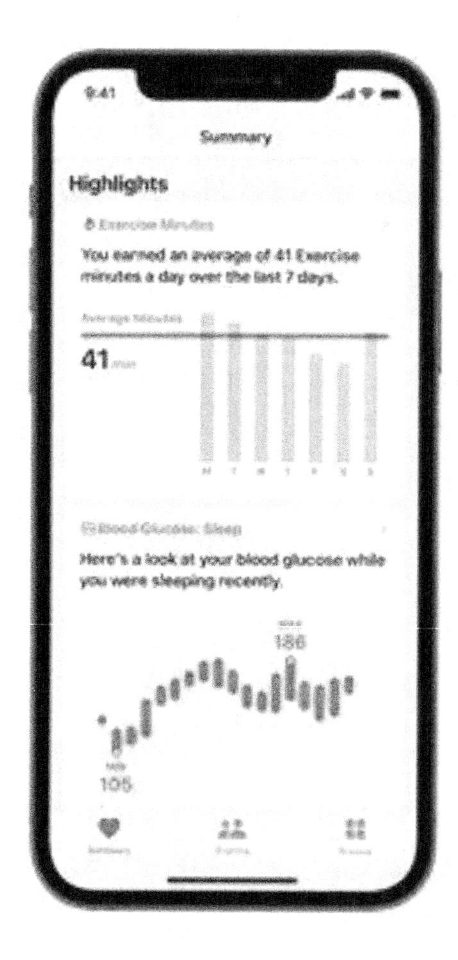

A summary screen displaying key information such as activity minutes and blood glucose levels when sleeping.

On the Summary page, you may add or delete a health category from your Favorites:

- At the bottom left, click Summary.
- To access the Favorites area, tap Edit.
- To switch a category on or off, touch it, then hit Done.

View The Latest Trends, Highlights, And Specifics For A Certain Health Category

To show the Health Categories page, tap Browse in the lower right, then one of these:

- Select a category. (Scroll up and down to view all categories.)
- Simply tap the search area and enter the name of a category (for example, body measurements) or a particular kind of data (such as temperature).

Cardio fitness, double support time, step length, walking asymmetry, and walking speed are all included in the Mobility category.

Depending on the data type, you may be able to do the following:

View more details about any of the data: Choose the Details option.

View weekly, monthly, and annual statistics: Tap the tabs at the top of the screen.

Manually enter data: Tap Add Data in the upper-right corner of the screen.

Add the following data type to the Favorites list on the Summary page: Add to Favorites should be turned on. (You may need to scroll all the way to the bottom.)

Determine which applications and devices can exchange data: Select Data Sources & Access from the Options drop-down menu. (You may need to scroll all the way to the bottom.)

To delete data, select Show All Data from the Options menu and then swipe left on a data record. To completely erase all data, select Edit, then Delete All.

Change the measurement unit: Tap Unit under Options to select a unit.

Improve your understanding of health and fitness:

The bottom section of the Summary screen contains introductory articles, app recommendations, and other information. Tap an item to get more information about it.

When you investigate the specifics of various health categories, suggested applications are displayed alongside your data.

How To Keep A Record Of Your Menstrual Cycle In Health On Your iPhone

Begin Monitoring Your Cycle

- At the lower right, click Browse, and then tap Cycle Tracking.
- Adhere to the prompts displayed on the screen after tapping Get Started.

Enter the necessary information about your last period to assist with improving estimates for your period and fertility window.

Maintain a Record of Your Cycle Statistics

Click Browse in the lower right corner, then Cycle Tracking.

Carry out one of the following:

It's as simple as tapping a day on the timeline at the top of the screen to keep track of a period day. To record the daily flow rate, select Period from the Cycle Log menu and then select an option.

Alternatively, in the upper right corner, select Add Period and then select days from the monthly calendar.

Logged days are represented on the timeline by solid red circles. To delete a logged day, tap it.

To keep track of symptoms, drag the timeline at the top of the screen to the desired day, then click Symptoms and check those that apply. When you're finished, click Done. Days with symptoms are indicated by purple dots.

Finding logs: Drag the timeline to the desired date, then tap Spotting, followed by Had Spotting.

By tapping Options and then selecting the categories, additional categories can be added.

Menstrual Cycle Predictions And Fertile Window

Click Browse in the lower right corner, then Cycle Tracking.

The timeline displays cycle forecasts based on previously recorded data. The following data is displayed:

Light red circles represent your period forecast.

To toggle between hiding and showing expected period days, go to Options and then Period Prediction.

Based on light blue days, this is a projection of your expected reproductive window. Predictions of fertility windows should not be used for birth control.

To turn on or off the fertile window prediction, go to Options and then Fertility Prediction.

The solid red rings represent the days of your menstruation.

The purple dots represent the days when you recorded symptoms.

Drag the timeline to select different days. The Cycle Log displays the information that you recorded on the selected day.

Cycle Control Factors

When you provide information about your pregnancy, nursing, and contraception use, it is used to help you manage your cycle forecasts.

Click Browse in the lower right corner, then Cycle Tracking.

Scroll down to the bottom and click Factors.

Carry out one of the following:

Factors influencing setup: Choose any factor that applies to you right now, and then click Done.

Add a variable: Tap Add Factor, select a factor, tap Started to change the start date, and then tap Add.

Change a current factor's expiration date: Select the factor, then End, select a date, and finally Done.

Remove a pre-existing factor: Select the factor, then click the Delete Factor button.

Previous factor logs are available here: Choose Show All.

To change the settings for period and fertility notifications, as well as other cycle monitoring options:

Click Browse in the lower right corner, then Cycle Tracking.

Scroll down to the bottom and click Options.

Press an option to activate or deactivate it.

To examine your cycle's history and statistics:

Click Browse in the lower right corner, then Cycle Tracking.

Scroll down to see timelines for the three most recent periods; keep scrolling to see associated statistics.

Click the Details button in the appropriate section of the page to see more information and historical data for Cycle History or Statistics.

Tap Filters at the upper right to see only the days in the detailed Cycle History that correspond to a specific symptom or flow level, then touch Done.

Chapter 10: iPhone SE Accessories

MagSafe Charger

Connect the MagSafe Charger to a power source using the Apple 20W USB-C adapter or any compatible converter (sold separately).

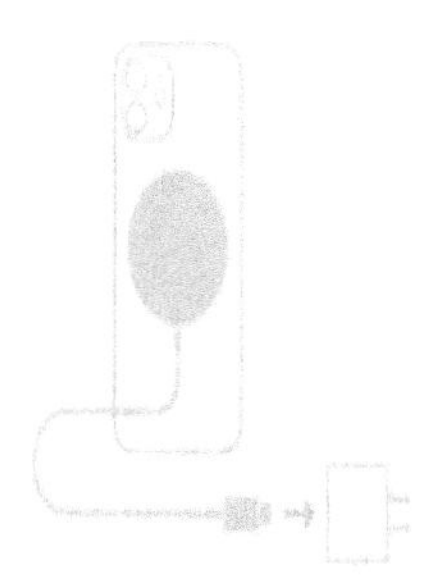

An example of the MagSafe Charger with one end connected to the rear of the iPhone and the other to a power converter.

Place the iPhone (supported models) face up in the MagSafe Charger's core. When the iPhone is correctly aligned with the charger, the status bar displays the Battery Charging icon.

MagSafe Duo Charger

With the MagSafe Duo Charger, you can simultaneously charge your iPhone (compatible models) or AirPods and your Apple Watch. (Apple Watch, MagSafe Duo Charger, and AirPods are offered separately.)

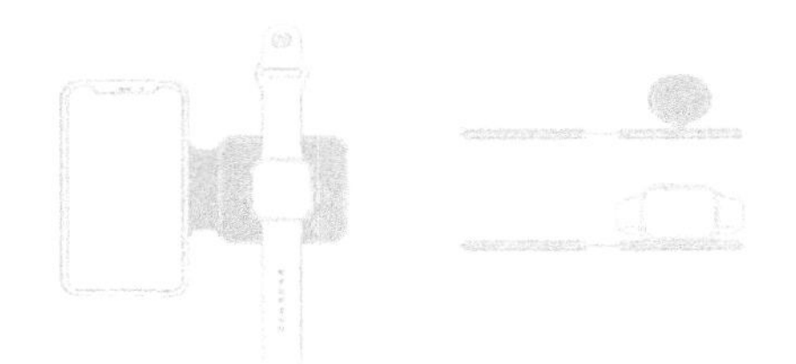

On the left, an iPhone and an Apple Watch are seen flat on the charging surfaces of the

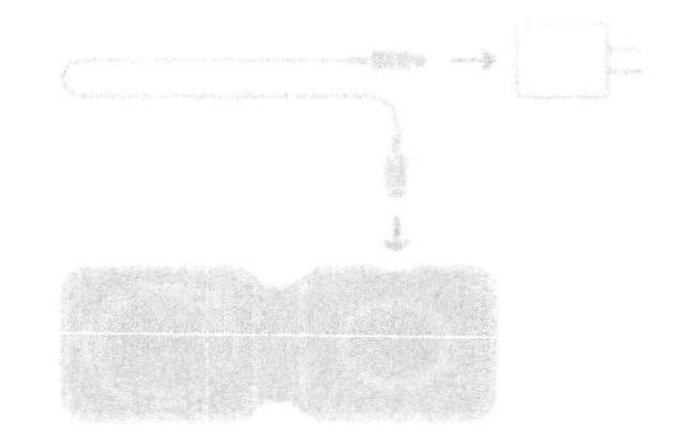

MagSafe Duo Charger. At the upper right, an image depicts the Apple Watch charging surface elevated. Apple Watch is positioned on the elevated charging surface in the image below.

Use the Apple 20W USB-C converter or any compatible adapter to connect the MagSafe Duo Charger to a power source (sold separately).

A cable with one end connected to a power adapter and the other to a MagSafe Duo Charger is shown.

One of the following methods is recommended for charging your iPhone or AirPods:

iPhone: Place the iPhone face up in the center of the iPhone charging surface. Magnets assist in aligning the device with the charger on iPhone 12 and later versions, and the charging sign appears when the device begins charging. When the iPhone is correctly aligned with the charging pad, the battery charging indicator appears on other versions such as the iPhone SE. Charging begins with a chime unless your iPhone is in silent mode.

NOTE: Remove the iPhone Leather Wallet if it is connected before putting the iPhone on the MagSafe Duo Charger.

Connect AirPods to your iPhone

- On the iPhone, go to Settings > Bluetooth and turn it on.
- Navigate to your iPhone's Home Screen.
- Take one of the following actions:

AirPods (1st, second, and third generations) or AirPods Pro: Open the cover to reveal your AirPods and place it close to your iPhone (iOS 15.1 or above is required for 3rd generation AirPods).

AirPods Max: Remove the Smart Case from your AirPods Max and place them next to your iPhone.

- Following the on-screen prompts, press Done.

Note: If you do not see on-screen pairing instructions for your AirPods Max, navigate to Settings > Bluetooth and select your AirPods. If the status light on your AirPods Max does not begin to flash white, press and hold the noise control button until it does.

Connect EarPods with iPhone

EarPods (available separately) may be used to listen to music and videos as well as to make phone calls on your iPhone. The EarPods are equipped with a microphone, volume controls, and a center button.

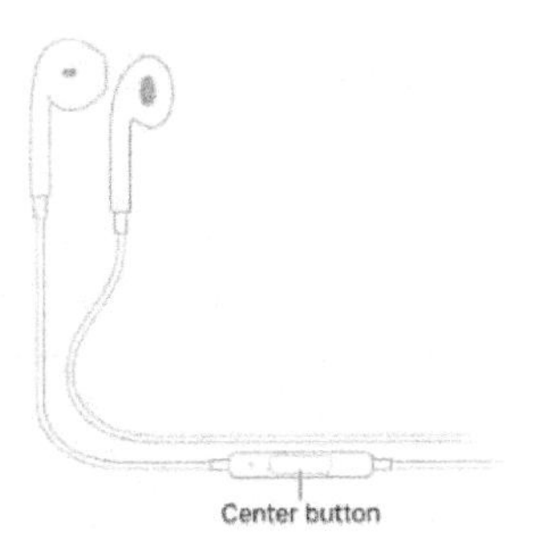

Apple EarPods; the middle button is on the wire that connects to the right earpiece.

Utilize your EarPods to control audio

- Press the middle button to pause. Press once more to resume playing.
- To skip forward, rapidly press the center button twice.
- To skip backward: rapidly press the center button three times.
- To fast-forward, press and hold the center button twice rapidly.

Use Earpods To Manage Calls

- Press the center button to answer an incoming call.
- Press the middle button to terminate the current call.
- Put the current call on hold and transfer to an incoming or on-hold call: Click the center button. Press once more to return to the first call.

Chapter 11: Apple Car Play, Apple Music

Apple Car Play

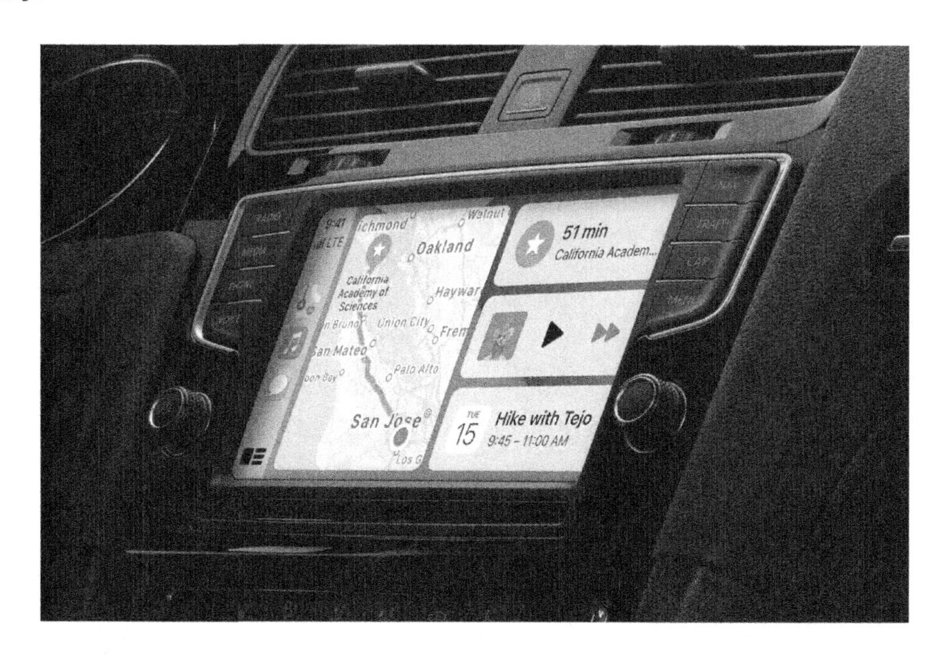

How To Link My iPhone To CarPlay

Set up CarPlay by connecting your iPhone and your car via the USB connection or wireless capabilities of your vehicle.

Check that Siri is turned on.

If your iPhone does not have Siri, go to Settings > Siri & Search and enable one of the following options:

Press the Home button to summon Siri.

Connect via USB:

Connect your iPhone to the USB port in your vehicle using an Apple-approved Lightning to USB cable.

On the USB port, the CarPlay logo or a smartphone image may be displayed.

Connect wirelessly:

In a car that supports wireless CarPlay, do one of the following:

For a few seconds, hold down the voice command button on your steering wheel.

Ascertain that your vehicle is in Bluetooth or wireless pairing mode.

On your iPhone, go to Settings > General > CarPlay > Available Cars.

Choose a mode of transportation.

Note: If your vehicle has wireless CarPlay capability, you can connect your iPhone by simply plugging it into the vehicle's USB port using a Lightning to USB cord. After starting CarPlay via USB, you'll be asked if you want to pair wireless CarPlay for future use if it's supported. If you accept, the next time you go on a trip, your iPhone will automatically connect to CarPlay.

After connecting to CarPlay on some electric vehicles, use the Maps app to identify the car for EV routing. Set up an electric vehicle route in iPhone Maps.

CarPlay Home appears instantly when you connect your iPhone to certain car types.

Select the CarPlay emblem on your vehicle's display if CarPlay Home does not show.

How To Use Siri In CarPlay

You may ask for anything you want using Siri voice control in CarPlay. (You can also use the built-in controls in your car to operate CarPlay.)

Use CarPlay to ask Siri questions.

Until Siri beeps, do one of the following:

1. On the steering wheel, press and hold the voice command button.
2. On a touchscreen with CarPlay enabled, press and hold the CarPlay Dashboard or CarPlay Home button.

Ask Siri a question or instruct her to do a task.

Say something like this to Siri:

- "Find out where the nearest coffee shop is."
- "Call Eliza Block,".
- "Songs like these should be played more often."
- "Show me the map,".
- "When do I have my next meeting?"
- "How is the forecast for today?"
- "When I come home, remind me to bring an umbrella."

Instead of waiting for Siri to realize that you've stopped speaking, push and hold the voice command button on the steering wheel while speaking, then release it when you're done.

In CarPlay, Siri also gives ideas for what you should do next, such as opening the garage door when you get home or driving to your next meeting.

How To Use Carplay To Make And Receive Phone Calls

From your iPhone, use CarPlay to make phone calls and listen to voicemail.

Say something like, "Call Eliza," to Siri.

You may also make a call using the built-in controls in your vehicle.

Select an option in CarPlay after opening Phone.

Note: If Phone isn't included in the recent applications list on the left when you're viewing CarPlay Dashboard, hit the Home button to see pages for all of your CarPlay apps, including Phone.

Apple Music

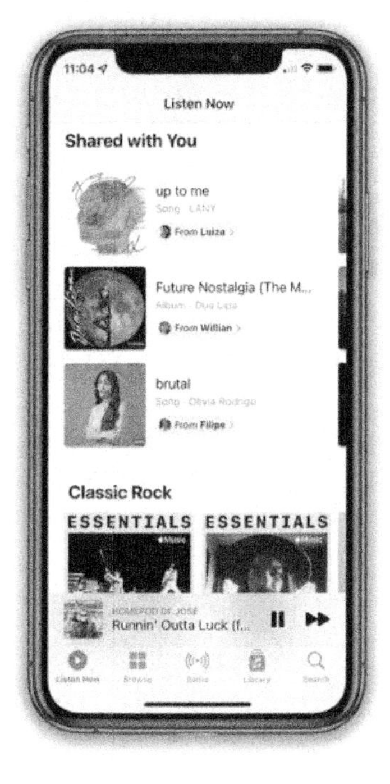

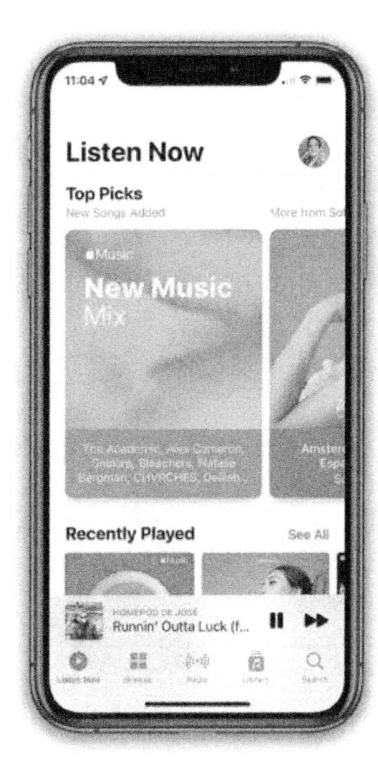

The Best Way to Hide Apple Music

Apple's Music service can be completely hidden. To do so, go to Settings> Music and uncheck Show Apple Music. When you open the app, you will only see your music, not any other music from the service.

How to Change the Library Categories

To clear a library and choose which categories, such as genres, artists, or songs, you want to see at a glance, tap the Edit button in the upper-right corner of the library screen, and then toggle the on/off settings.

Where Can I Find Downloaded Music?

Tap the Library tab in the app's menu bar at the bottom to see only music that is physically on your device, then tap Downloaded music.

How Do I Make A New Playlist?

Are you planning a trip and want to create a playlist? Tap the Library tab at the bottom of the application menu bar, then Playlists, then New Playlist. From there, you can enter a playlist name, description, music, and toggle whether or not the playlist is public.

Find Selected Apple Playlists

The "For You" tab in the bottom menu bar contains music templates selected by the Apple Music Group. Suggestions include a mix of favorites, daily playlists, featured artists, and new releases, all tailored to you and your musical tastes.

How to Find Apple Music

Touch the search icon in the bottom menu bar to open the dedicated search box, where you can manually enter artist names, album titles, and other information.

How to Discover the Best Playlists

To see a regularly updated list of Apple Music's most popular songs, go to the Browse tab in the menu bar at the bottom, and then tap Top Playlists.

How to Look for Videos

Apple Music is about more than just music. It also includes music videos and other video content. To watch new and top music videos on Apple Music, go to the Browse tab in the bottom menu bar, and then scroll down to Videos.

How to Locate Radio Stations

Apple Beats, in addition to Beats 1, offers stations based on genres and various themes. You can find them at the bottom of the menu bar under the Radio tab. Simply tap "Radio Station" from there.

How to Share an Album

Do you want to share an album on Twitter, Facebook, or somewhere else? Touch any album, then tap the three-dot (...) button at the top. Tap Share album and then select how you want to share it.

Add An Album To Your Offline Library

Select Add to Library after tapping the album. When you're finished, tap the down arrow on the cloud to load it.

How to Appreciate an Album

Apple Music can tell if you like an album so that it can tailor its music recommendations to you. Select the three-dot button ( ) after touching any album (). Touch Love from there.

How to Make a Station Out of a Song

Touch any song, then, in the music management menu (tap it at the bottom to expand it into a full-screen tab), select the three-dot (...) button in the top right corner. Then, select Create Station. This will launch a radio station based on this unique song.

Including A Song In A Playlist

Tap any song, then tap the three-dot (...) button at the top of the music management menu (tap it at the bottom to expand it to a full-screen tab). Tap Add to playlist and then select which playlist you want to add to (old or new).

Add A Song To Your Offline Library

To add a song to your library, tap the "+" symbol next to it. You can then download the song by clicking the cloud with the arrow.

How to View a Song's Lyrics

Do you understand what the artist says in the song? Apple Music allows you to view lyrics. Play any song, then tap the bottom of the screen to expand the controls to a full-screen tab. The letters will appear on their own.

Change a Song's Audio Source

Do you want to switch from your iPhone to the connected speaker? Play any song, then click the radio wave arrow (located below the volume slider). Select the audio source from the drop-down menu.

Share the Artist

Artists, like songs and albums, can be shared with a friend via social media and messaging apps. Touch the three-dot button (() next to any artist's name and select Artist Share. Choose how you want to share from there.

Chapter 12: Best Tips And Tricks

The following are some of the top tips and tricks for the iPhone SE 3 2022 that you can use to get the most out of your brand-new gadget.

Measure someone's height

This amusing gimmick for the iPhone SE 2022 makes use of Apple's augmented reality capabilities. Simply put, you can use your iPhone to measure the height of another person in a quick and accurate manner. Simply launch the Measure app and make sure the person whose dimensions you're attempting to capture is visible across the entire display screen. If everything is done correctly, you should see a line appear above the person's head. The answer to this question will reveal their height. If you need to save the snapshot for later use, you can do so by tapping the white shutter button on the right.

Personalize your home screen by including a widget

One of the most anticipated new features of iOS 15 is the ability to finally add widgets to one's home screen. You can now add widgets to your home screen by touching and holding an empty spot on the screen, then clicking the + symbol in the top left corner of the screen. Before you can change the widget's current layout and add it to the home screen, you must first search for and locate it.

Activate the "Assistive Touch" feature

If your phone has assistive touch, you will find it much easier to operate it with just one hand. Go to the Settings menu, then Access, and finally Touch. You will be able to use assistive touch from that point. If you enable the feature, your phone will be more accessible when you use it. It is not necessary to pull down the screen until you reach the top of the screen and then glide down to access the notification center. You can simply tap it. You can even activate Siri, bring up the control center by tapping the screen, and do a variety of other things like lock your phone, rotate the screen, change the volume up or down, take a screenshot, and so on. With Assistive Touch, you can also change the gestures for single-tapping, double-tapping, and long-pressing. You are even permitted to create your own hand gesture.

Hide or uninstall an app from the Home screen

Long press the Apps icon you want to hide or remove from your home screen, and then tap the minus symbol that appears at the top of the screen. This allows you to hide or remove an app from your home screen. You will be given two options: delete the app completely or remove it from the home screen. If you no longer need the application, you can remove it from the home screen by selecting "Remove" or "Delete app," but you should not uninstall it. If you move an app from the home screen to another location, you can quickly and easily find it using Spotlight or the App Library.

Photo and Selfie in a Hurry

Navigate to the Home screen and look for the camera symbol. When you tap and hold the camera icon, a popup appears with options like "Take Selfie," "Record Video," "Take Portrait," and "Take Portrait Selfie." Hold your finger on the camera icon. From the lock screen, long-pressing the camera symbol on the right side of the screen or sliding to the right will quickly take you to the camera. You can quickly access the camera from the lock screen, ensuring that you never miss a photo opportunity. It is not necessary for you to unlock your phone in order for someone else to photograph you using it. This implies that there is no possibility of a violation of privacy.

For Burst Mode, use Volume Up

Burst Mode allows you to take multiple shots in rapid succession. If you enjoy using this camera feature, you can take pictures with more control by pressing the volume up button. Select the Camera option from the Settings menu on your iPhone SE 3. Then, toggle the Use Volume Up for Burst Mode switch to the on position.

Take a picture and a video at the same time

You can take a photo and a video on your iPhone simultaneously by employing a clever technique. To start recording a video, make contact with and keep your finger on the shutter button. When the video recording is finished, release your finger from the shutter button to return to photo mode.

Keep your notes secure

Personal notes require extra security to prevent unauthorized individuals from accessing them. As a result, it is in everyone's best interest to keep them locked at all times so that no one else can enter. Open the Notes app on your iPhone, then navigate to the note you want to lock. Then, in the upper right corner of the screen, tap the More button (the icon with three dots) to select the Lock button for the share sheet. The next step is to assign a password to your locked notes. If you want to use Touch ID to manage locked notes, go to the Settings app, then to Notes, then to Password, and finally to Use Touch ID.

Scanning documents

You will have no trouble scanning any papers you require using the document scanner included with the Apple Notes app on your iPhone SE. Launch the Notes app, then choose a note to view. When you touch any part of the screen after that, the keyboard will appear. Then, from the drop-down menu that appears after clicking the camera icon, select Scan Documents. The paper should then be moved into view, and the shutter button should be depressed.

Hide your photographs

Do you no longer want others to be able to view your private images? Don't be alarmed. You can choose to hide all of your personal images from view. Launch the Photos app on your iPhone, and then tap the Select button in the upper right corner. Then, choose which images you want to keep hidden. After that, click the Sharing button and choose "Hide in the share sheet" from the menu that appears. Navigate to the Photos section after opening the Settings app. To hide the secret album within the Photos app, tap the toggle next to Hidden Album and then toggle it off.

Chapter 13: Maintenance And Battery Replacement Options

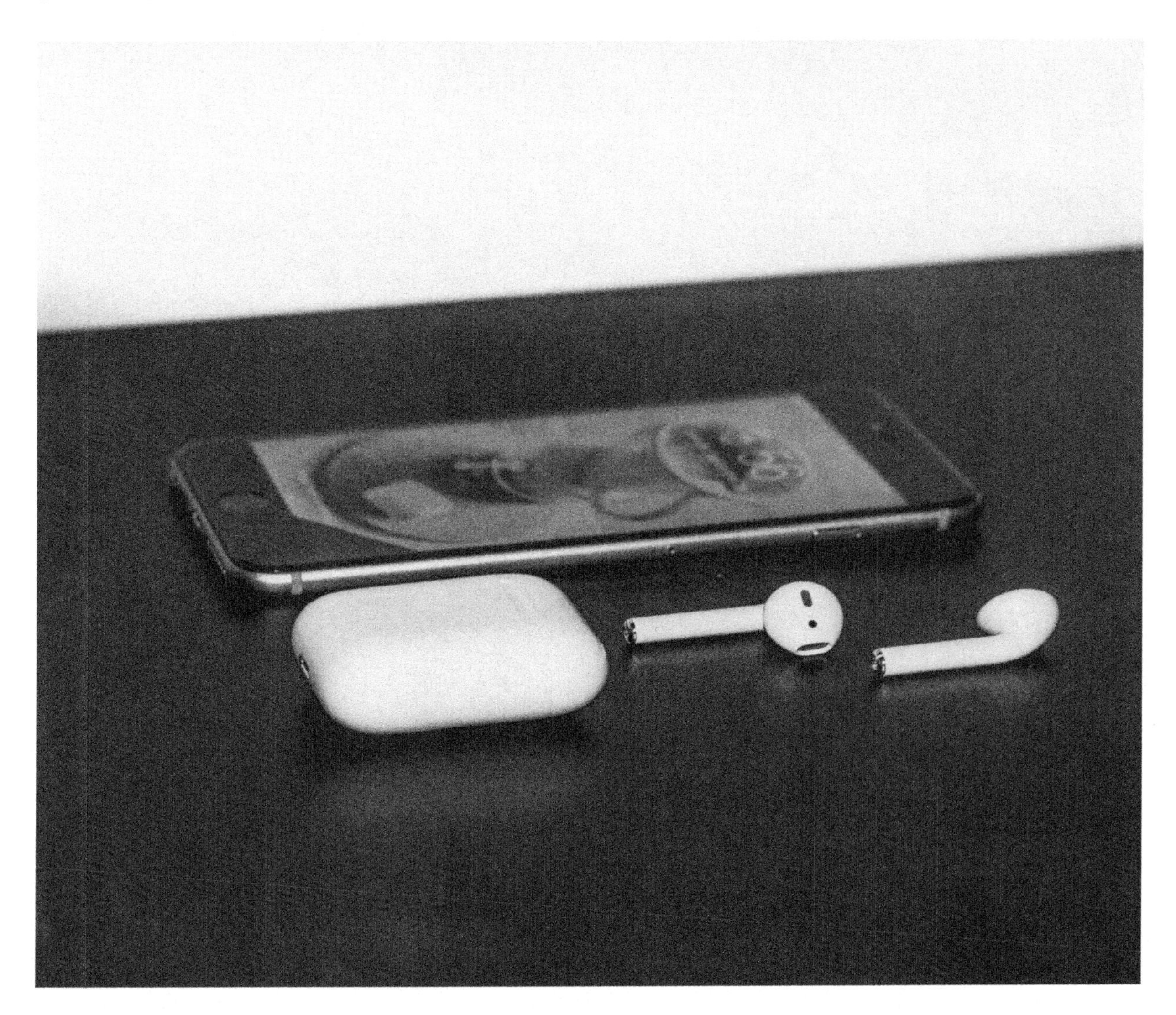

iPhone features an internal lithium-ion rechargeable battery that provides the best performance for your device at the moment. In comparison to conventional batteries, lithium-ion batteries are smaller, lighter, faster to charge, last longer, and have a higher power density for increased battery life.

How to Charge The Battery

To charge your iPhone, choose one of the following methods.

- Utilize the charging cable and an Apple USB power adapter to connect the iPhone to a power outlet.

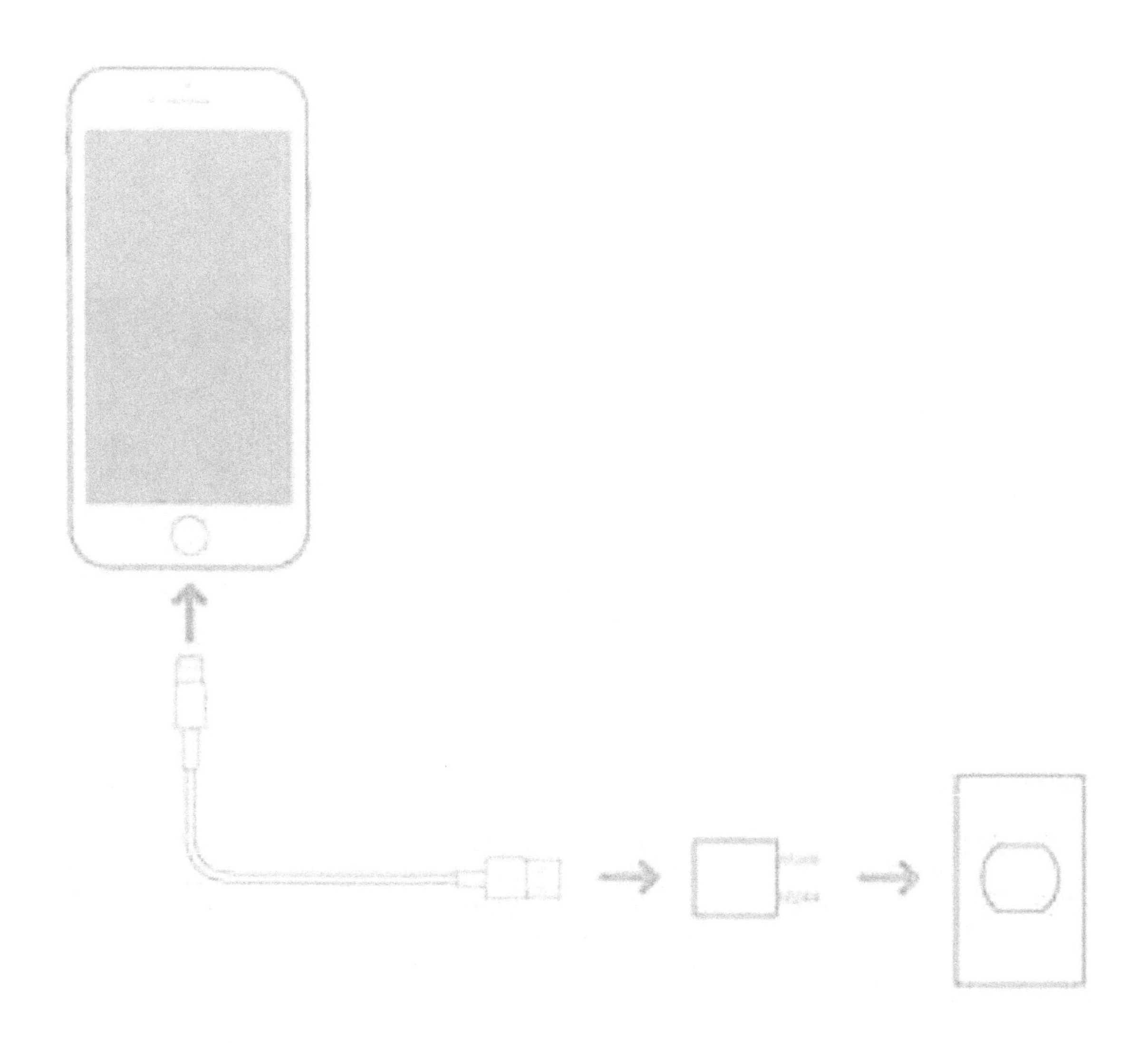

- Using a cord, connect your device to your computer.

Switch to Low Power Mode

Using Low Power Mode significantly extends the life of the battery charge. Switch to Low Power Mode when your iPhone's battery is low or you don't have access to electricity.

To access the battery settings, follow these steps:

Navigate to Settings.

Select Battery.

Change to Low Power Mode.

Low Power Mode turns off unnecessary background activity and optimizes performance for critical tasks like making and receiving calls, emails, and messages, as well as browsing the internet.

Improve Battery Charging

The iPhone has a setting that helps to slow the rate of battery aging by reducing the time the battery is fully charged. This setting uses machine learning to determine your daily charging routine and then delays charging above 80% until you need it.

Navigate to Settings.

Select Battery.

Select Battery Health.

Turn on Optimum Battery Charging.

Battery Percentage Can Be Found In The Status Bar

Navigate to Settings.

Select Battery.

Turn on Battery Percentage.

Examine The Battery's Condition

To access the battery settings, follow these steps:

Navigate to Settings.

Select Battery.

Select Battery Health.

iPhone displays information about your battery's capacity and peak performance, as well as whether it needs to be serviced.

View Statistics on Battery Consumption

Navigate to Settings.

Select Battery.

Information on your battery usage and activities for the previous 24 hours and up to 10 days is displayed.

Suggestions and observations: You can view information about the conditions or usage habits that contribute to the energy consumption of your iPhone. You may also receive energy-saving recommendations. If a suggestion appears, click it to access the appropriate setting.

Last Charged: This indicates how fully charged the battery was and when it was last unplugged.

Battery Level Graph (for the last 24 hours): This shows the battery level, charging intervals, and times when the iPhone was in Low Power Mode or the battery was dangerously low.

Battery Usage Graph (for the last ten days): This shows the percentage of battery power consumed daily.

Activity Graph: Shows activity over time, divided into segments based on whether or not the screen was turned on.

Screen On/Off: Shows overall activity for the specified time period, including when the screen was turned on and off. The daily average is displayed in the Last 10 Days view.

Battery Usage by App: Shows the percentage of battery life consumed by each application over the specified time period.

Activity by App: Shows the amount of time spent on each app within the specified time frame.

Note: To view battery information for a specific hour or day, select the time period from the graph. Deselect the graph by tapping outside of it.

Chapter 14: Air Tag - What It Is And How To Set It Up

AirTag is a Bluetooth tracker that can be attached to personal items. It is about the size of a coin and can be easily hung with any item. For example, if you hang it with a key, the phone will make a sound and display a warning if the key leaves a certain range of the paired iPhone. If you do not receive the alert the first time, you can locate the lost key by following the steps in the iPhone's "Find My" app.

In other words, this is a Bluetooth location tracker. Simply hang it with the important items you want to track, and you'll be able to prevent loss. Put it with your iPad, wallet, key, handbag, and so on. If you misplace it, you can track it down using the iPhone's "Find My" feature.

Setup

Apple AirTag is a small button-built tool designed to link to items such as keys and wallets so that these apps can be tracked down using Apple's "Find My" app and Apple-enabled Bluetooth.

If you have a new AirTag, you must set it up and configure it before you can use it. Please ensure that your iPhone or iPad has been updated to iOS 14.5 or iPadOS 14.5 before performing this operation. Check your iOS version by going to Settings -> General -> Software Updates.

How to Install AirTag on iPhone?

1. Make sure your "iPhone" is turned on and the home screen is displayed.

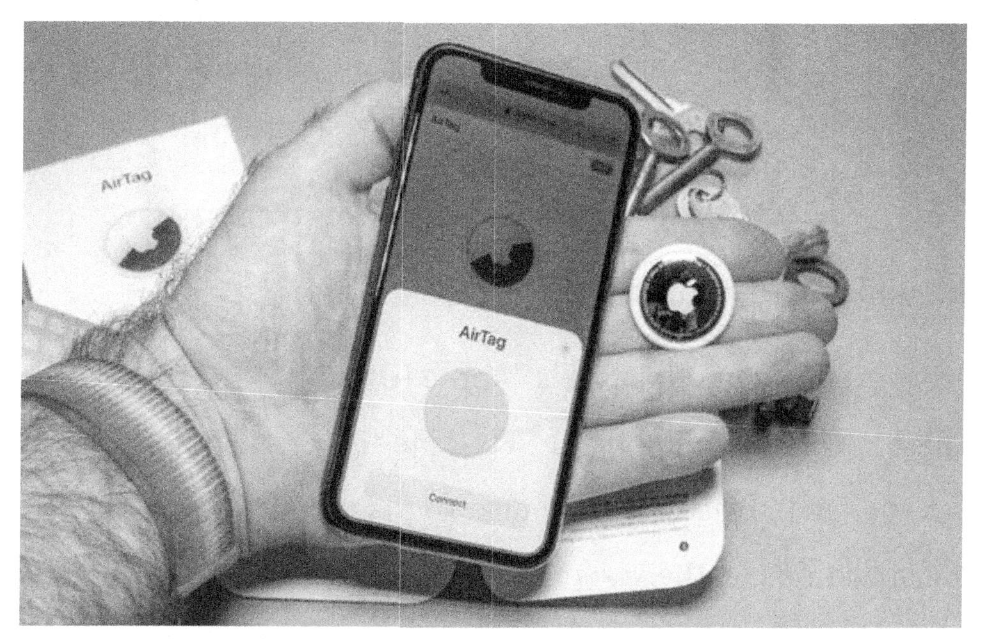

2. If the battery label is not removed from AirTag, move it closer to the iPhone
3. On the card from the screen, click "Connect."
4. Choose a name from the list, or click "Custom Name" to enter a name and select emoji, then click "Continue."
5. Click "Continue" to register the item on your Apple ID, then click "Finish".

How to Add AirTag to "Find My"?

If necessary, you can subscribe to the new AirTag directly from the "Find My" app.

1. Start "I found" and click on "Project".
2. Scroll to the bottom of the "Items" menu and click "Add New Item".

3. Click Add AirTag and follow the instructions on the screen.

If AirTag is already registered in someone else's "Apple ID", they need to disconnect it before installing it. They can do the following in "Find Me" on their "iPhone": tap the item, then tap AirTag to delete it. Place the item next to the iPhone, then tap Delete item, then follow the instructions on the screen.

Chapter 15: Frequently Asked Questions

How To Move Data From iPhone To iPhone SE 2022

Transfer Data to a New iPhone Using Quick Start

Keep in mind that QuickStart will take up space on both the regular iPhone and the iPhone SE, rendering them inoperable if not removed.

Keep your new iPhone near your old iPhone. The QuickStart screen appears on your existing iPhone, allowing you to set up the iPhone SE with your Apple ID.

Touch Continue after you confirm that you want to use the Apple ID. Check that Bluetooth is turned on if you don't see the option to continue on your current device.

An animation will appear on your new iPhone > Place your old iPhone on top of your new iPhone and use the viewfinder to focus the animation.

If you are unable to use your iPhone's built-in camera, select Verify manually. You'll receive an authentication code on your new iPhone; enter that code on your old iPhone.

Enter your most recent iPhone passcode on the new iPhone.

Follow the on-screen instructions to set up Touch ID on your new iPhone SE. Enter your Apple ID password on your new iPhone if prompted.

You can restore apps, data, and settings from your most recent iCloud backup to your new device, then restore your current device backup. You can also transfer your location, privacy, Apple Pay, and Siri preferences.

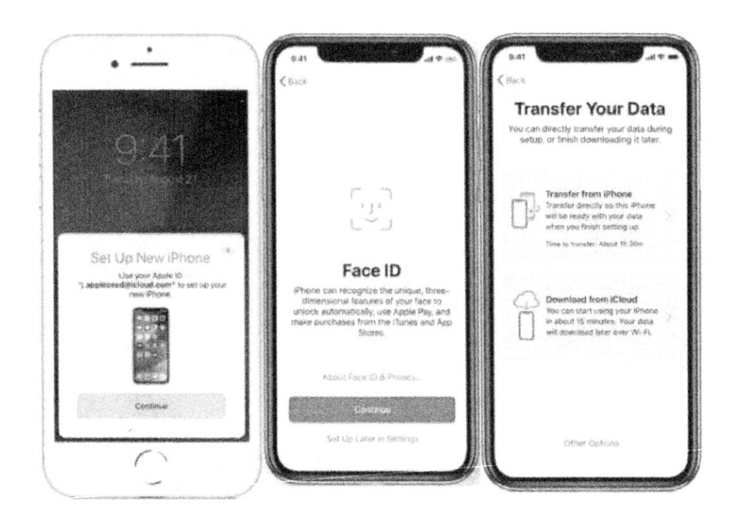

Select Move from iPhone to move your data from your old iPhone to your new iPhone SE without a backup if your prior iPhone is running iOS 12.4 or later.

How To Perform A Hard Reset On An Apple iPhone SE (2022) Using the Recovery Mode Without a Password

This is the strategy to use if an issue prevents the phone from starting. In such instances, recovery mode is utilized to conduct a hard reset without a password.

1. Please switch off your phone if it is turned on.
2. Press and hold the power and volume down keys simultaneously (if nothing happens, try the article on how to enter recovery mode).

3. Instead of a standard loading screen, you will see a menu that can be explored by using the volume keys (to move the mouse) and the power button (to select).
4. Select "Wipe data/factory reset" using the power button.

5. To complete the reset, click the "Yes" option.

When the reset is finished, the device will reboot and display the regular setup window and welcome. Again, depending on your device, the titles of the menus may differ significantly.

Why Isn't My Apple iPhone SE (2022) Turning On?

There are several possible causes for the device's inability to function consistently; problems frequently arise during normal use. According to experts and device manufacturers, the following conditions may result in boot failures:

Some system files were installed incorrectly after updating the operating system; the device would not boot up due to viruses introduced with programs that were not downloaded directly from the Play Market; the screen or battery cord fell out after the smartphone was dropped on a hard surface; the USB port became blocked, or moisture formed small yet dangerous rust spots on the inside.

It should be noted right away that dealing with only physical harm is a difficult task. When you attempt to repair the smartphone yourself, you may inadvertently break some connections, rendering the device unrepairable. If the procedures listed below do not produce a satisfactory result, it is recommended that you contact a verified MC for diagnostic and repair.

How to Use a Cable to Connect an iPhone SE 2022 to a Screen

You can connect your iPhone to a secondary display such as a computer monitor, TV, or projector using the appropriate adapter or adaptor.

Connect to your TV using a Lightning Digital AV Receiver:

Insert a Lightning Digital AV Adapter or a Lightning to VGA Adapter into the iPhone's bottom charging port.

Connect your phone to a television using an HDMI or VGA cable:

The other end of your HDMI or VGA cable should be connected to your monitor, TV, or projector.

If necessary, change the video source on your monitor, TV, or projector to the appropriate one. If you need help, refer to the instructions on your screen.

Using a second socket on the adapters, you can plug in a charging cable and charge your iPhone while it's connected to a monitor, TV, or projector.

Mirroring Your iPhone SE To An Apple TV Or Smart TV

What's on your iPhone might be visible on Apple TV or a smart TV.

Activate the Control Center software on your iPhone.

Select your Apple TV or an AirPlay 2-compatible Smart TV as the playback location by pressing the Screen Mirroring button.

Any AirPlay passwords that appear on the TV screen should be entered into your iPhone.

To return to the iPhone, open Control Center, then select Screen Mirroring, then Stop Mirroring.

How to Connect a Magic Keyboard

Check that the keyboard is turned on and charged.

Navigate to Settings > Bluetooth on the iPhone and enable Bluetooth.

Select the device when it appears in the Other Devices list.

How to Listen to Audio from an iPhone SE on a Bluetooth Audio Device

Select an item to play by opening an audio app on your iPhone, such as Music.

Tap the Play destination button to select your Bluetooth device.

You can change the replay destination on the lock screen or in the Control Center while the music is playing. The playback destination returns to iPhone when you move the device out of Bluetooth range.

Conclusion

Thank you for reading this book. Nowadays, everyone wants to own an iPhone. The craze for iPhones has reached a fever pitch in recent years, which is understandable given its fantastic features. The iPhone SE 3 is the latest addition to the SE line, and despite its unappealing design, the iPhone SE 3 still packs top-notch features in a small package. You'll be pleased to learn that the iPhone SE 3 has a powerful 12mp camera as well as an A15 Bionic processor. The A15 Bionic processor is the same one found in the most recent iPhone models, such as the 13 Pro Max.

Aside from its fantastic features, the iPhone SE 3 can be used by seniors for a variety of day-to-day tasks. Imagine a phone that can track your health and the health of your family members, all of this and more is included when you purchase an iPhone SE 3 or any other iPhone.

Have fun using your new device!

Printed in Great Britain
by Amazon